I've said this before, but, even though time goes by very fast in the series and the story takes place in the future, please think of it as all occurring in the present.

—Tsugumi Ohba

I actually get more excited drawing the series within the series rather than the main series.

—Takeshi Obata

Tsugumi Ohba

Born in Tokyo, Tsugumi Ohba is the author of the hit series *Death Note*. His current series *Bakuman。* is serialized in *Weekly Shonen Jump*.

Takeshi Obata

Takeshi Obata was born in 1969 in Niigata, Japan, and is the artist of the wildly popular SHONEN JUMP title *Hikaru no Go*, which won the 2003 Tezuka Osamu Cultural Prize: Shinsei "New Hope" award and the 2000 Shogakukan Manga award. Obata is also the artist of *Arabian Majin Bokentan Lamp Lamp*, *Ayatsuri Sakon*, *Cyborg Jichan G.*, and the smash hit manga *Death Note*. His current series *Bakuman。* is serialized in *Weekly Shonen Jump*.

Volume 16

SHONEN JUMP Manga Edition

Story by **TSUGUMI OHBA**
Art by **TAKESHI OBATA**

Translation | **Tetsuichiro Miyaki**
Touch-up Art & Lettering | **James Gaubatz**
Design | **Fawn Lau**
Editor | **Alexis Kirsch**

Printed in the U.S.A.

Published by VIZ Media, LLC
P.O. Box 77010
San Francisco, CA 94107

10 9 8 7 6 5 4 3 2 1
First printing, November 2012

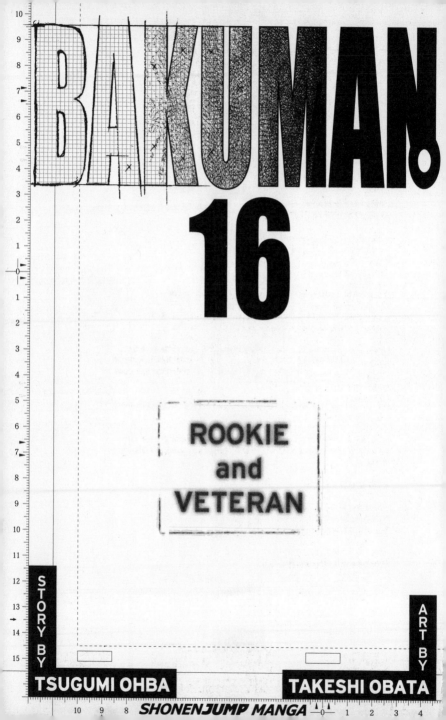

UMAN. バクマン。vol.16

D C B A

STORY In order to attain the glory that only a handful of people can, two young men decide to walk the rough "path of manga" and become professional manga creators. This is the story of a great artist, Moritaka Mashiro, a talented writer, Akito Takagi, and their quest to become manga legends!

WEEKLY SHONEN JUMP Editorial Department

1 Editor in Chief Sasaki
2 Deputy Editor in Chief Heishi
3 Soichi Aida
4 Yujiro Hattori
5 Akira Hattori
6 Koji Yoshida
7 Goro Miura
8 Masakazu Yamahisa
9 Kosugi

The MANGA ARTISTS and ASSISTANTS

A SHINTA FUKUDA
B KO AOKI
C AIKO IWASE
D KAZUYA HIRAMARU
E RYU SHIZUKA
F NATSUMI KATO
G YASUOKA
H SHOYO TAKAHAMA
I TAKURO NAKAI
J SHUICHI MORIYA
K SHUN SHIRATORI
L ICHIRIKI ORIHARA
M TOHRU NANAMINE
N MIKIHIKO AZUMA

AND FOR THE SAKE OF THOSE FANS...

FANS ARE GREAT, AREN'T THEY?

JUST LOOK AT ALL THIS NEW MAIL FROM HAPPY FANS.

YOU MADE THE RIGHT DECISION IN DOING THE STORY ABOUT A COPYCAT.

YOU JUMPED ALL THE WAY UP TO THIRD PLACE.

CHAPTER 134 FRONT RUNNER AND SLOW RUNNER

BOTH MASHIRO AND I CAME UP WITH THE SAME IDEA AS TO WHAT WE HAD TO DO AS MUTO ASHIROGI.

WE BOTH GOT THE IDEA OF CREATING A STORY ABOUT A COPYCAT AND HOW PCP REJECTS THEM.

I SEE. AS ALWAYS, YOU TWO ARE IN PERFECT SYNC WITH EACH OTHER.

I NEVER IMAGINED...

AND I'M GOING TO TELL YOU THIS NOW, BUT...

...THERE WERE PEOPLE WITHIN THE EDITORIAL DEPARTMENT WHO SAID IT WOULD BE DANGEROUS TO DO A STORY LIKE THAT.

BUT I CONVINCED THEM THAT IT WAS TO SHOW THAT ASHIROGI WOULD NEVER GIVE IN TO ACTIONS LIKE THIS AND THAT I'D TAKE RESPONSIBILITY IF SOMETHING HAPPENED. AND THE EDITORIAL DEPARTMENT FINALLY REALIZED THAT THEY NEEDED TO BE PROTECTING YOU AND NOT THE COPYCAT.

WHAT?

THEY SAID IT MIGHT LOOK LIKE YOU WERE TRYING TO PROVOKE THE COPYCAT EVEN WHEN THAT PERSON HADN'T BEEN CAUGHT YET.

I'M GRATEFUL THAT NIZUMA SEES YOU AS A RIVAL IN A GOOD WAY.

RIGHT...

HE MUST HAVE DONE IT TO CHEER US UP...

AND NIZUMA PLAYED A BIG PART IN THIS TOO. WE JUST COULDN'T SIT STILL AFTER LEARNING THAT *CROW* RECEIVED FIRST PLACE.

SHFF SHFF

NIZUMA REWRITES HIS STORY-BOARDS?!

UNTIL NOW, HE HAD BEEN CREATING HIS STORYBOARDS IN A FLASH, BUT I'VE BEEN TOLD THAT HE'S BEEN SPENDING DAYS CONTEMPLATING AND REWRITING THEM.

HE'S RECEIVED FIRST PLACE THREE WEEKS IN A ROW...

AT ANY RATE, NIZUMA IS JUST AMAZING.

...

AERIAL PRISON ARC EDITS GEKIMAN!!

CROW
Eiji Nizuma

JUST BECAUSE MAINSTREAM BATTLE MANGA HAVE BEEN THE MOST POPULAR IN *JUMP* UNTIL NOW DOESN'T MEAN IT'S ABSOLUTE.

AFTER ALL, THERE HAVE BEEN TIMES WHEN A GAG MANGA LIKE *DR. SLUMP* GOT FIRST PLACE.

NAH. I'M STARTING TO FEEL THAT DOING OUR BEST ISN'T ENOUGH TO BEAT A MAINSTREAM BATTLE MANGA...

LET'S JUST KEEP TRYING.

I WISH WE COULD BEAT HIM.

EIJI NIZUMA IS ALWAYS ABOVE US...

SIIIGH...

RIGHT.

AND IT SOUNDS CLOSE WHEN YOU HEAR ABOUT *CROW* BEING IN FIRST PLACE AND *PCP* BEING IN THIRD, BUT IN ACTUALITY, THERE IS A 150-VOTE DIFFERENCE BETWEEN THE TWO.

HMM. BUT THE MAINSTREAM BATTLE MANGA HAVE ALWAYS BEEN ON TOP THESE DAYS...

I'M STARTING TO FEEL THE LIMIT OF A NON-MAINSTREAM, CULT HIT MANGA...

...

WE'LL INCH OUR WAY UP A LITTLE BIT AT A TIME.

HN?

A LITTLE BIT AT A TIME...

I'VE FINALLY GOTTEN MYSELF BACK TOGETHER AGAIN, SO I'LL DO MY BEST.

YEAH!

THANK YOU VERY MUCH.

THE FINAL DRAFT FOR *+NATURAL*.

THE FINAL DRAFT FOR *CROW*.

SHUP

SHUP

NIZUMA
Eiji Co.,
Ltd

I KNOW THAT THE ARTWORK IS FINE... YOU'RE NOT CUTTING CORNERS OR SLACKING OFF WITH THE ART, BUT...

I'M DOING THE BEST I CAN ON IT. IS SOMETHING WRONG?

SHF SHF

CAN YOU DO SOMETHING ABOUT *NATURAL TOO?

UMM, NIZUMA...

SHF SHF

SWIP

*NATURAL ...

EVEN THOUGH YOU DO THE ARTWORK FOR BOTH OF THEM...

IT RECEIVED TENTH PLACE THIS WEEK... *CROW GOT FIRST PLACE AND *NATURAL GOT TENTH PLACE.

1

10

ITS RANK SUDDENLY DROPPED AS SOON AS THE ANIME ENDED.

IF YOU WANT IT TO BE POPULAR, YOU HAVE TO CREATE A GOOD STORY TOGETHER WITH AKINA SENSEI, MR. MIURA.

I'M NOT THE STORYWRITER FOR THAT.

WELL...

OKAY...

SHF SHF

PSSST

...DOESN'T HAVE AN INTERESTING STORY.

I THOUGHT SO TOO. EVEN THE GREAT YOSHIDA COULDN'T SOLVE THIS ONE.

WHAT? FIND A GIRL FOR NAKAI? *IMPOSSIBLE!*

TMP TMP

DING DONG

OH! SPEAK OF THE DEVIL.

...

IF I CAN GO ABOUT THIS THE RIGHT WAY...

NO, WAIT A MINUTE...

...

BUT... IF I HAVE YOU DO THAT, I WILL HAVE TO PUT AN END TO MY PLANS FOR YOU TO EAT AWAY HIRAMARU'S MONEY SO HE'D FEEL ECONOMICALLY PRESSURED...

....!

BUT BEFORE THAT, YOU'RE GOING TO HAVE TO GO THROUGH A DIET REGIMEN I WILL CREATE FOR YOU...

HMM...

O-OF COURSE.

DO YOU SERIOUSLY WANT A GIRL-FRIEND?

NOD NOD

...

AND IT'LL BE EVEN WORSE IF YOU WERE TO GET SICK OR SOMETHING. YOUR SKILLS ARE TOO GOOD TO BE HIRAMARU'S ASSISTANT, AFTER ALL...

BUT NO MATTER HOW MUCH NAKAI EATS, THE MONEY SPENT ON THE FEED... I MEAN, FOOD, DOESN'T HAVE A VERY STRONG NEGATIVE EFFECT ON HIRAMARU RIGHT NOW...

IS THAT WHAT YOU WERE THINKING OF, MR. YOSHIDA?!

WHAT?

...

?

14

CROW'S DOING GREAT...

YEAH!! *CROW* IN FIRST PLACE FOR FOUR CONSECUTIVE WEEKS!!

FRIDAY, APRIL 22

WELL, THE STORY IS REALLY EXCITING RIGHT NOW WITH ALL THE CHARACTERS INVOLVED IN A FINAL BATTLE-TYPE EVENT.

PCP RECEIVED THIRD PLACE... THE DIFFERENCE WITH CROW HASN'T CHANGED... THE ANIME FOR ROAD RACER GIRI STARTED, BUT EVEN THAT RECEIVED EIGHT LESS VOTES...

...

WELL, EVEN IF +NATURAL FAILS, I'VE STILL GOT MIKATA'S JUSTICE, WHICH WILL JUMP UP THE RANKS ONCE THE TV DRAMA STARTS...

MIKATA'S JUSTICE GOT SEVENTH PLACE... +NATURAL, THIRTEENTH PLACE...

I- I SEE! SO THAT'S WHAT IT MEANS!

WHAT...?

THEY SAID *CROW'S* FIRST PLACE CHEERED THEM UP.

ASHIROGI WANTED TO THANK NIZUMA.

OH, YUJIRO.

HUH? WHAT DO YOU MEAN?

WHAT?

THURS-DAY, APRIL 28

YUJIRO, *CROW* GOT FIRST PLACE AGAIN.

WHAT?

BUT IT'S THURS-DAY TODAY, ISN'T IT?

OH, WE'VE GOT GOLDEN WEEK FROM TOMOR-ROW, SO THE RESULTS ARE ALREADY OUT.

SHIZUKA RECEIVED TENTH PLACE... MISS AOKI RECEIVED SEVENTH PLACE...

CAN'T FOOL ME GOT FIFTH PLACE. GOOD! THAT'S JUST THE RIGHT PLACE TO BE FOR NOW!

(SIGN: SHUEISHA)

FIRST PLACE FOR FIVE WEEKS IN A ROW!

MY TIME HAS COME...

I'M YUJIRO HATTORI, IN CHARGE OF THE SERIES IN FIRST AND THIRD!

I THINK IT'S ABOUT TIME I WAS PROMOTED TO A CAPTAIN!

IT'S TOO OLD-FASHIONED TO SAY THAT I'M STILL TOO YOUNG!

AND NIZUMA HASN'T SAID ANYTHING WEIRD EVEN THOUGH HE'S BEEN GETTING FIRST PLACE RECENTLY.

THE ANIME IS STARTING TO BOOST ITS RANK UP.

ROAD RACER *GIRI* GOT THIRD PLACE TOO...

AMAZING...

GRIN

HE'S GETTING TOO CARRIED AWAY...

BUT WE CAN'T COMPLAIN CUZ HE'S GETTING RESULTS.

PCP RECEIVED FOURTH PLACE. THAT'S FINE BUT... IS IT IMPOSSIBLE TO BEAT AN ANIMATED SERIES... LET ALONE NIZUMA...?

GIRI HAS MOVED ABOVE THEM...

MIURA, DON'T BE SO HAPPY AND DO SOMETHING ABOUT *+NATURAL.*

YES, SIR.

GOOD! *MIKATA'S JUSTICE* GOT SIXTH PLACE!

I'M GOING DOWN TO GET THE FINAL DRAFT FROM FUKUDA AND MEET WITH HIM.

VIP

SHA—

WHAAAT?! THE RIGHT TO END ANY SERIES HE DOESN'T LIKE?!

...

SINCE I'VE TOLD FUKUDA AND YASUOKA ABOUT IT ALREADY...

OH... WELL, I GUESS I CAN TELL YOU.

WHAT DO YOU MEAN?

?

I WAS WORRIED AT FIRST, THOUGH.

FIRST PLACE FOR FIVE WEEKS IN A ROW... PRETTY IMPRESSIVE, MASTER NIZUMA...

AND? AND? WHICH SERIES DOES NIZUMA SENSEI WANT TO END?

...AND THE EDITOR IN CHIEF SAID IF HE STILL FELT THE SAME WAY AFTER BECOMING THE TOP STAR OF *JUMP*...

OF COURSE, I TOLD HIM THAT IT WOULD BE IMPOSSIBLE...

I'M BLOWN AWAY...

OH, I HAVEN'T ASKED HIM THAT...

YOU GOTTA TELL US.

MISS AKINA IS TOO PROUD TO CHANGE HER STORIES, SO HE SEEMS TO THINK THAT IT WOULD BE BETTER TO END IT RATHER THAN PROLONG THE SERIES.

NIZUMA SAID THE STORY WASN'T GOOD.

NATU-RAL?! WHY'S THAT?

RIGHT... OR IT COULD JUST BE *NATURAL* NOW...

BUT IF HE SAID THAT BEFORE GETTING HIS OWN SERIES... THAT'S SEVEN YEARS AGO, RIGHT? IT COULD BE A SERIES THAT'S ALREADY ENDED.

DON'T BE STUPID. MASTER NIZUMA ISN'T THAT FREAKIN' PETTY!

OR MAYBE IT'S EITHER *GOD GIVEN* OR *CAN'T FOOL ME*, SINCE HE WAS CRUSHED BY THOSE TWO AT THE LOVE FEST.

AS A MATTER OF FACT, HE SAID IT WOULD BE BETTER IF HE CREATED THE STORIES FOR IT.

BUT HE MAY DISLIKE IT EVEN MORE BECAUSE IT IS HIS SERIES.

HE'D NEVER CHOOSE TO END HIS OWN SERIES, WOULD HE?

I CAN TALK ABOUT IT NOW THAT I KNOW IT ISN'T AN ISSUE.

WHAT? THEN WHY DID YOU BRING IT UP?

AND EVEN IF NIZUMA WAS THE MOST POPULAR MANGA ARTIST RIGHT NOW, HE PROBABLY ISN'T THINKING ABOUT ENDING A SERIES ANYMORE, AND WON'T SAY SOMETHING LIKE THAT.

IF WE INCLUDED THE CONTRIBUTION OF THAT MANGA ARTIST AND THE SALES OF THE GRAPHIC NOVELS, NIZUMA STILL HAS A LONG WAY TO GO.

IT'S MEANINGLESS TO TALK ABOUT THIS ANYWAY. WE DON'T EVEN KNOW HOW TO DETERMINE WHO THE MOST POPULAR MANGA ARTIST IN *JUMP* IS.

TRUE THAT!

I GUESS MASTER NIZUMA IS THAT KIND OF GUY, BUT IF HE COULD GET FIRST PLACE THAT EASILY, HE SHOULD HAVE DONE SO A LOT EARLIER.

...

PLUS I KNOW THE REASON HE WENT AFTER FIRST PLACE WITH *CROW* AT THE BEGINNING WAS TO CHEER ASHIROGI UP.

IT JUST SHOWS HOW MUCH NIZUMA'S GROWN WHILE WORKING ON HIS OWN SERIES.

WE WERE TOLD THAT IT WAS HARD TO GET A SPONSOR BECAUSE OF THE CONTENT...

WHAT? WHY'S THAT?

THE STORY IS GETTING CLIMACTIC WITH AN ALL-OUT BATTLE BREAKING LOOSE.

WOW. *CROW* GOT FIRST PLACE FOR FIVE WEEKS IN A ROW.

AND THAT BANK BREAK-IN THE OTHER DAY PRETTY MUCH SEALED ITS FATE.

SIGH... COMPARED TO THAT, *PCP* WON'T EVEN BECOME AN ANIME...

WHAT

...

MY DRAWING SPEED'S IMPROVED EVEN MORE BECAUSE YOU'VE BEEN SO LATE RECENTLY...

SAIKO, MAYBE IT'S TIME WE SERIOUSLY STARTED THINKING ABOUT ANOTHER SERIES...

LET ME TAKE A LOOK AT THEM.

LIKE I SAID, THEY'RE LACKING.

LET ME BE THE JUDGE.

SHFF

OH? BUT THIS ONE LOOKS GOOD, DOESN'T IT? AND THIS ONE TOO!

NO... THEY HAVE TO JUMP OUT.

...TO USE IN A CULT-HIT BATTLE MANGA USING MAINSTREAM CHARACTERS, BUT NONE OF THEM STRIKE A CHORD...

AND I'VE BEEN DESIGNING CHARACTERS...

OHBA'S STORYBOARD

OBATA'S STORYBOARD

COMPLETE!

※CREATOR STORYBOARDS AND
FINISHED PAGES IN JAPANESE

BAKUMAN。vol.16
"Until the Final Draft Is Complete"
Chapter 134, pp. 18-19

YOU'RE THE ONLY ONE LEFT, HAYABUSA!!

ALL RIGHT, HERE IT COMES! GIRI'S SPECIAL MOVE; TRIANGLE FLY CORNERING!!

Oooh, my Giri is flying!

GW o o o o

DO IT.

SORRY.

LET ME ENJOY MY SHOW FOR A CHANGE.

MR. YUJIRO, DO YOU HAVE TO COME TO PICK UP THE FINAL DRAFT EVERY TIME THE ANIME IS ON...?

HE CAME WHEN THE ANIME IS RUNNING AGAIN... AND AT THE BEST PART TOO.

YUJIRO'S HERE FOR THE FINAL DRAFT.

GLOOM—...

? ? ?

I'LL WAIT UNTIL IT'S OVER.

ROLL...

27

MASTER NIZUMA ASKED YOU GUYS FOR PERMISSION TO END A SERIES HE DOESN'T LIKE, DIDN'T HE?

W-WHAT ARE YOU TALKING ABOUT?!

WHERE'S YOUR PROOF?

GULP!!

HERE.

FWAP

FWAP

W-WHERE'S THE FINAL DRAFT?!

MR. YUJIRO SAID IT WOULD PROBABLY BE +NATURAL LAST WEEK.

IN THAT CASE, WHICH SERIES DOES MASTER NIZUMA WANT TO END...?

HE'S SO EASY TO READ...

BAM

TH-THANKS...

NOW, S-STOP JUMPING TO CONCLUSIONS AND DON'T SPREAD ANY STUPID RUMORS.

CLOMP CLOMP CLOMP CLOMP

29

31

BUT WE STILL DON'T KNOW IF NIZUMA WAS GIVEN THE RIGHT TO END A SERIES, RIGHT?

YEAH.

福田
FUKUDA

...

WHY DO YOU SOUND SO HAPPY ABOUT IT...?

THE TWO TALKED IN PRIVATE IN ANOTHER ROOM, SO EVEN MR. YOSHIDA, A CAPTAIN, DOESN'T KNOW WHAT THEY TALKED ABOUT.

I GOT THIS INFORMATION FROM MR. YOSHIDA.

BUT IT IS CERTAIN THAT NIZUMA DROPPED BY THE EDITORIAL DEPARTMENT ON MONDAY AND TALKED WITH THE EDITOR IN CHIEF.

SHUP

...

WELL, THAT WAS YUJIRO'S GUESS, SO I WOULDN'T BE TOO SURE ABOUT IT...

AND THAT IS +NATURAL...

AND YUJIRO HAS BEEN ACTING VERY STRANGELY... SO, I WOULDN'T BE SURPRISED IF HE WAS GIVEN THE RIGHT TO END ANY MANGA HE WANTS TO.

IN OTHER WORDS, THE CONTENT OF THAT CONVERSATION WAS ONLY TOLD TO YUJIRO, WHO IS MASTER NIZUMA'S EDITOR.

...

OH... I MEANT WHAT SHOULD I DO IF IT WAS MY WORK, THAT'S ALL...

YOU MUSTN'T SOUND SO HAPPY, HIRAMARU.

SH-FF SH-FF

NO, IT MIGHT ACTUALLY BE CAN'T FOOL ME!

IS THAT WHY MR. MIURA SEEMED TO HAVE GIVEN UP...?

BUT ALL THIS TALK ABOUT HIM RECEIVING THAT RIGHT AND THE WORK BEING +NATURAL IS ALL JUST SPECULATION, RIGHT?

HALF OF +NATURAL MAY BELONG TO NIZUMA...

I FIND IT HARD TO BELIEVE THAT HE WOULD BE GIVEN THE RIGHT TO END SOMEONE ELSE'S WORK NO MATTER HOW MANY TIMES HE MAY HAVE GOTTEN FIRST PLACE.

...

YEAH!

LET'S GO.

RIGHT. WE CAN SETTLE THIS BY GOING OVER TO HIS PLACE AND ASKING HIM STRAIGHT UP!

I'LL GO AND ASK NIZUMA IN PERSON.

IT'S MEANINGLESS TO TALK ABOUT IT HERE.

...

VSH

WHAT?

SHA

36

THAT I WILL CHOOSE WHEN TO END THE SERIES MYSELF AND WILL END IT WHEN THE POPULARITY OF THE WORK IS AT ITS PEAK.

BUT I HAD DECIDED THIS FROM BEFORE I STARTED MY SERIES.

I KNOW THE EDITORIAL DEPARTMENT DOESN'T WANT TO END A POPULAR SERIES. THEIR JOB IS TO SELL A MAGAZINE, SO THAT'S TOTALLY EXPECTED.

I HATE NOT BEING ABLE TO END A SERIES THE WAY I WANT TO.

!

I'M GLAD BECAUSE IT LOOKS LIKE I'LL BE ABLE TO DO THAT NOW.

THE EDITOR IN CHIEF INITIALLY TRIED TO PERSUADE ME TO CONTINUE WORKING ON IT, BUT I CONVINCED HIM IN THE END.

...

SCRCH
SCRCH

NOT EXACTLY.

AND THAT'S WHY HE SAID YOU COULD END THE SERIES UNDER THE CONDITION THAT YOU GET FIRST PLACE FOR TEN WEEKS IN A ROW...?

...

WHAT IF YOU FAIL TO GET FIRST PLACE FOR TEN CONSECUTIVE WEEKS...?

AND THE EDITOR IN CHIEF ACCEPTED IT.

IF I GET FIRST PLACE FOR TEN CONSECUTIVE WEEKS, I WILL THEN WRAP UP THE SERIES IN ANOTHER TEN WEEKS AFTER THAT. THAT IS THE CONDITION I PROPOSED TO HIM.

THE END

PLEASE LOOK FORWARD TO NIIZUMA SENSEI'S ...

SHWIIN

OR GET CANCELED...

YOU EITHER END AS THE DOMINANT SERIES...

THAT'S PRETTY EXTREME.

...

THEN I WON'T END THE SERIES.

IT WOULDN'T BE COOL TO LET ANOTHER MANGA GET AHEAD OF ME, AND THAT WOULD NOT BE THE PERFECT END IN MY EYES.

SWIP

I'M GOING TO LEAVE SINCE YOU'RE NOT THINKING OF ENDING +NATURAL...

EXCUSE ME.

BAM

SHE NEVER CHANGES ...

AND IF I CANNOT EVEN DO THAT, I MAY JUST HAVE TO CONTINUE THE SERIES UNTIL THE EDITORIAL DEPARTMENT DECIDES TO DROP IT.

SO, IF THAT HAPPENS, I WILL CHALLENGE MYSELF TO DOMINATE THE FIRST PLACE POSITION FOR MORE THAN TEN WEEKS BEFORE ENDING THE SERIES.

AFTER ALL, THE ANIME IS STILL RUNNING.

IT'S GONNA HURT *JUMP* IF *CROW* ENDS NOW...

IN SOME WAYS, YOU ARE BEING SELFISH...

OR SHOULD YOU END A SERIES WHEN YOU WANT TO END IT...?

SHOULD YOU CONTINUE A SERIES BECAUSE IT'S POPULAR?

BUT THIS IS A VERY DIFFICULT QUESTION.

UNLESS YOU'VE GOT A GOOD REASON LIKE WHEN ASHIROGI SENSEI DECIDED TO END *TANTO* BECAUSE IT DIDN'T SUIT THEM, OR IF YOU'VE GOT SOME OTHER WORK THAT YOU WANT TO CREATE EVEN MORE THAN *CROW*...

IN MY OPINION, IT'S A WASTE TO END A SERIES WHILE IT'S STILL POPULAR.

I CAN ONLY THINK ABOUT ENDING *CROW* IN A PERFECT WAY AT THIS POINT.

NOTHING IN PARTICULAR.

...

MASTER NIZUMA, HAVE YOU DECIDED ON WHAT TO CREATE NEXT?

39

LABOR IS SOMETHING YOU DO JUST TO EARN ENOUGH MONEY TO MAKE A LIVING AND...

HE SHOULD QUIT HIS JOB AND PLAY AROUND AT ONCE!

NIZUMA HAS ENOUGH MONEY TO SPEND HIS LIFE IN LEISURE NOW.

WHAT ARE YOU TALKING ABOUT?!

VSH

BUT THERE'S NO GUARANTEE THAT YOU'LL EVEN BE ABLE TO CREATE ANOTHER SMASH HIT WITH YOUR NEXT WORK.

YOU SHOULD CONTINUE THE SERIES AS LONG AS IT'S POPULAR...

BUT I'M NOT ALLOWED TO DRAW AS FREELY AS I WANT TO FOR +NATURAL, AND IT DOESN'T EXACTLY FEEL LIKE MY WORK...

YES.

WELL, EVEN IF YOU END CROW, YOU'VE STILL GOT +NATURAL, SO YOU CAN WORK HARD ON THAT...

OH, RIGHT...

HIRAMARU, WE'RE NOT TALKING ABOUT THAT RIGHT NOW.

HUMPH

...SO I WOULD LIKE TO DO SOMETHING ELSE ONE DAY.

SKRT

I JUST CAN'T SWALLOW IT.

...BUT I DON'T WANT YOU TO END IT LIKE THIS.

I AIN'T AGAINST YOU ENDING CROW IN YOUR IDEAL WAY...

!

SKRT

SKRT

BUT THINK ABOUT IT THIS WAY.

MAYBE THAT'S WHAT IT LOOKS LIKE TO YOU...

COMING HERE'S LIT A FIRE UNDER US.

SKRT

SKRT

CROW IS ENTERING ITS GREATEST CLIMAX EVER— YOU'LL NEVER BE ABLE TO BEAT IT!

AND DO YOU SERIOUSLY THINK PEOPLE WHO HAVE PUT THEIR STORY-BOARDS AND FINAL DRAFTS ASIDE TO COME HERE CAN ACTUALLY BEAT ME?!

I ACCEPT THAT CHALLENGE! I AIN'T GONNA LET YOU END YOUR SERIES IN SUCH A COOL WAY.

SKRT

SKRT

SKRT

SKRT

RIGHT !!

WE WON'T LET YOU!

EEEEK

SKRT SKRT

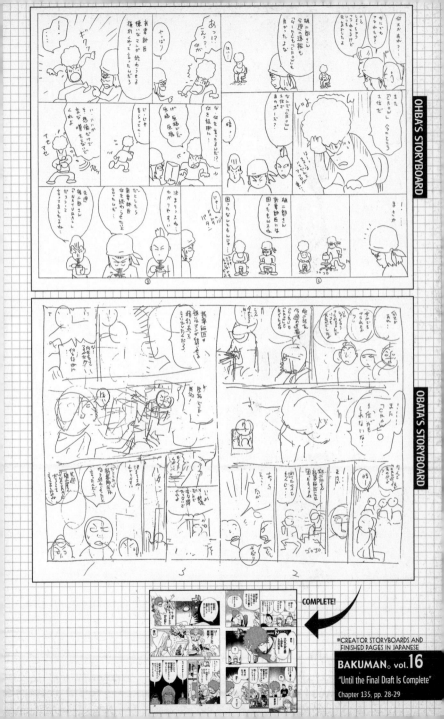

OHBA'S STORYBOARD

OBATA'S STORYBOARD

COMPLETE!

※CREATOR STORYBOARDS AND
FINISHED PAGES IN JAPANESE

BAKUMAN。vol.16
"Until the Final Draft Is Complete"
Chapter 135, pp. 28-29

CHAPTER 136
POTENTIAL AND COUNTERPLAN

BUT IF HE ISN'T SUCCESSFUL IN GETTING FIRST PLACE RIGHT BEFORE THE FINAL CHAPTER, WE'D END UP WITH A SERIES THAT'S SCHEDULED TO END NOT ACTUALLY ENDING... WON'T THAT CAUSE TROUBLE? WELL, I'M SURE WE CAN DEAL WITH IT SINCE THAT'LL MEAN THE MANGA CAN CONTINUE.

YES. PLEASE TELL THE EDITOR IN CHIEF ABOUT THE CHANGE.

IT'S NOT JUST TEN WEEKS IN A ROW NOW? YOU'RE GOING TO KEEP GETTING FIRST PLACE UNTIL THE FINAL CHAPTER?

WHAT ?!

...

What do you mean?

NIZUM
Eiji Co.
L+

THAT'S RIGHT.

...YOU'LL NEED TO GET FIRST PLACE FOR SEVENTEEN OR EIGHTEEN WEEKS IN A ROW...

UMM... BUT THAT MEANS...

AND THEY TOLD ME, "WE'LL GET FIRST PLACE TO STOP YOU FROM ENDING CROW."

THAT'S WHAT I TOLD THE MEMBERS OF TEAM FUKUDA.

...

I FEEL EVEN MORE MOTIVATED NOW. I WILL NEVER LOSE TO THEM.

NO?

NO. I DON'T THINK THAT'S GOING TO WORK.

THEN REALLY JUICE UP THE CONCLUSION OF THOSE ARCS TO GET FIRST PLACE.

...WE SHOULD CREATE A FOUR-CHAPTER ARC AND A THREE-CHAPTER LONG ARC.

IF WE HAVE SEVEN CHAPTERS...

...

WE'VE USED THAT METHOD MANY TIMES BEFORE, AND WE'VE NEVER GOTTEN ABOVE *CROW* WITH IT.

GOOD POINT.

HOW CAN WE MOVE ABOVE *CROW*...?

IN THAT CASE, WHAT CAN WE DO?

I THINK WE NEED TO MAKE IT EVEN LESS MAINSTREAM.

I'M JUST SAYING WE SHOULD TRY TO BRAINSTORM IN THAT DIRECTION.

BUT WHAT SPECIFI-CALLY DO YOU CHANGE...?

NANA-MINE'S *WHAT YOU NEED* HAS ENDED TOO, SO THERE AREN'T ANY OTHER SIMILAR SERIES RUNNING!

SO, WE SHOULD EMPHASIZE THAT DIFFERENCE IN OUR MANGA AND TRY OUR LUCK WITH THAT!!

CROW IS A TYPICAL MAINSTREAM BATTLE MANGA. AND IF WE SEE *PCP'S* STRONGEST POINT BEING THAT IT'S A CULT HIT, WE'LL HAVE THE BEST CHANCES OF COMPETING AGAINST CROW WITH THAT!

LESS MAIN-STREAM...?

BA

AM

52

MURMUR

NO, I DON'T WANT IT TO END EITHER.

THAT'S NOT POSSIBLE. THINK ABOUT THE FINANCIAL HIT WE'LL TAKE...

HE WANTS TO END CROW?

MURMUR

MURMUR

onen Ju

Jump

V Squ

MURMUR

WHAT THE?

NAKANO, YOU'RE SUCH A COMPANY MAN!

DON'T BE AB-SURD!

AS LONG AS THEIR WORK IS PLACED IN A COMMERCIALLY PUBLISHED MAGAZINE, THE MANGA DOESN'T ONLY BELONG TO THE CREATOR.

THE MANGA ARTISTS ARE THE CREATORS, SO IT'S TRUE THAT THE MANGA BELONGS TO THEM.

BUT I THINK IT'S FOR THE GOOD OF THE MANGA ARTIST AND SERIES TO LET THEM END THE STORY WHERE THEY WANT TO.

MURMUR

MURMUR

CROW IS ONE OF OUR SIGNATURE SERIES...

MURMUR

IT'S TOTAL CHAOS HERE.

WE SHOULDN'T END *CROW* FOR NIZUMA'S SAKE!

WHAT ARE YOU ALL TALKING ABOUT? THIS ISN'T EVEN ABOUT COMPANY PROFITS!

BUT I GUESS THIS ALL BOILS DOWN TO WHETHER AN EDITOR SHOULD WORK FOR THE MANGA ARTIST OR WORK FOR THE COMPANY'S PROFITS AT A TIME LIKE THIS. AFTER ALL, WE ARE CORPORATE EMPLOYEES...

54

VERY FUNNY!! YOU JUST STARTED THE SERIES. IT'S TEN YEARS EARLY FOR YOU TO TELL ME THAT YOU WANT TO END IT.

ZWIK

BY THE WAY, MR. YOSHIDA, AS A PROFESSIONAL MANGA ARTIST I THINK *CAN'T FOOL ME* SHOULD...

...

I AM SO TOUCHED BY NIZUMA. A TRUE MANGA ARTIST SHOULD END THEIR SERIES WHEN THEY WANT TO.

HIRAMARU

平丸

SHING SHING

...IS TO STOP *CROW* FROM ENDING.

LOOK, HIRAMARU. YOUR JOB, RIGHT NOW...

BIP

BIP

EXACTLY!

WHAT...

YOU'RE TELLING ME TO GET FIRST PLACE?!

NO... WHY IS THAT?

BUT IT STILL FEELS LIKE A GAG MANGA. YOU KNOW WHY; DON'T YOU?

I'VE BEEN CREATING THIS SERIES FROM THE START WITH THAT IMAGE.

FROM NOW ON, *CAN'T FOOL ME* IS GOING TO BECOME A STORY MANGA WITH LAUGHS AND TEARS.

STILL?

THAT'S GOING TO BE IMPOSSIBLE! YOU ALWAYS SAY YOURSELF THAT "THIS IS A GAG MANGA! YOU'D NEVER BE ABLE TO GET FIRST PLACE WITH IT!"

BIP

BIP BIP

PLIP

THAT'S RIGHT... IT IS STILL A GAG MANGA...

WOW! THIS LOOKS GREAT, FUKUDA!!

HE'S BASICALLY AN OUTLAW RACER WHO TURNS ANY LOCATION INTO A RACECOURSE!

SO THIS OLD MAN IS THE LEGENDARY RACER WHO HAS NEVER BEEN DEFEATED!!

I LIKE HIM. AND I LIKE THE NEW MEMBERS AS WELL!'

BUT THE MOST IMPORTANT THING IN THIS ARC... AND IN A SHONEN MANGA MAGAZINE...

WHAT DO YOU MEAN DREAM? I'M GONNA MAKE IT INTO REALITY!!

ADDING AN ATTRACTIVE NEW CHARACTER TO WIN POPULARITY! THAT'S A COMMON PRACTICE. BUT YOU'RE ALSO INTRODUCING A NEW BIKE! NOW IT WON'T BE JUST A DREAM FOR YOU TO MOVE ABOVE *CROW*!

YEAH, YOU KNOW YOUR THING, MR. YUJIRO!!

IS THE DESIGN OF THE NEW MOTORBIKE!!

A NEW CHARACTER ?!

A CULT HIT MAINSTREAM BATTLE MANGA...

I'VE ALWAYS BEEN THINKING ABOUT IT IN THE CORNER OF MY HEAD...

BUT IN ORDER TO HAVE A COOL CHARACTER, WHO'D FIT RIGHT IN AS THE MAIN CHARACTER OF A MAINSTREAM BATTLE MANGA, EXIST IN A NON-MAINSTREAM BATTLE MANGA...

...THAT CHARACTER WILL HAVE TO BE A DARK ANTIHERO.

YEAH.

I CAME TO THE SAME CONCLUSION AS YOU!

YEAH, BUT THAT'S...

...FOR SOMETHING WE SHOULD CREATE NEXT. WE HAVE TO BEAT *CROW* WITH *PCP* FIRST.

BUT THE LAST GUY WAS JUST ONE OF THE STUDENTS, SO HE WASN'T A VERY ATTRACTIVE EVIL CHARACTER...

YOU'RE RIGHT!

I GOT THE IDEA WHEN I WAS WORKING ON THE COPYCAT ARC. EVIL CHARACTERS TEND TO STAND OUT A LOT!!

I'M SAYING WE SHOULD INTRODUCE A CHARACTER LIKE THAT IN *PCP*!

CAN YOU TELL? WHOOPIE!

SENSEI, DID YOU GET THE IDEA FOR THE DESIGN OF THIS BIKE FROM TORIYAMA SENSEI?

FUKUDA WORKED ON HIS NEW CHARACTERS AND MOTORBIKE...

WHOOPIE...?

OOOH, COOL!!

HOW'S THIS FOR THE CHARACTER?

SO WE CREATED A MYSTERIOUS NEW CHARACTER NAMED SIGMA FOR ISSUE 26, WHICH WILL COME OUT ON MAY 30.

WEEKLY JACK

SWIP

YES, NAKAI SENSEI...

YOU JUST CAN'T DRAW PROPERLY, CAN YOU?

REDRAW THIS.

HIRAMARU IMPROVED HIS ARTWORK...

WHAP

WHAP

TAKAHAMA CREATED A STORY ABOUT THE MAIN CHARACTER'S FRIEND BEING FALSELY ACCUSED...

SKRT

SKRT

!

WHOA, GIRI INTRODUCED A NEW CHARACTER TOO!

YES.

AND ON MAY 24, THE SAMPLES OF ISSUE 26 WITH OUR PRIZED NEW IDEAS WERE DELIVERED TO US.

CROW GOT FIRST PLACE ON ISSUES 24 AND 25, BUT THIS ISSUE 26 IS GOING TO REALLY DECIDE THE OUTCOME OF THINGS.

66

THIS IS ALL THANKS TO YUJIRO. I MAY BE IMAGINING IT, BUT I THINK THE QUALITY OF MOST OF THE LINEUP HAS IMPROVED COMPARED TO PREVIOUS ISSUES.

W-WHAT?! YOU'RE RIGHT...

H-HIRAMARU'S ARTWORK'S IMPROVED!

AS FAR AS I CAN TELL... ALL THE MANGA ARTISTS WHO WENT DOWN TO NIZUMA'S PLACE HAVE TRIED SOMETHING NEW...

YOU GOT THIS, BOSS.

YES!

SHA

I'M GOLD, RIGHT?

WE'RE GOING TO SURPASS EIJI!

YEAH!!

WELL DONE, HIRAMARU... YOU'RE JUST LAZY. MAKE AN EFFORT AND YOU CAN ACTUALLY GET THINGS DONE. JUST LOOK AT HOW MUCH YOUR ARTWORK HAS IMPROVED.

Heh heh...

IT'S ALL FOR KAZUTAN...

BUT I'M SURE I'LL MOVE UP QUITE A BIT WITH THIS.

THREE MORE CHAPTERS UNTIL THE COURTROOM TWIST...

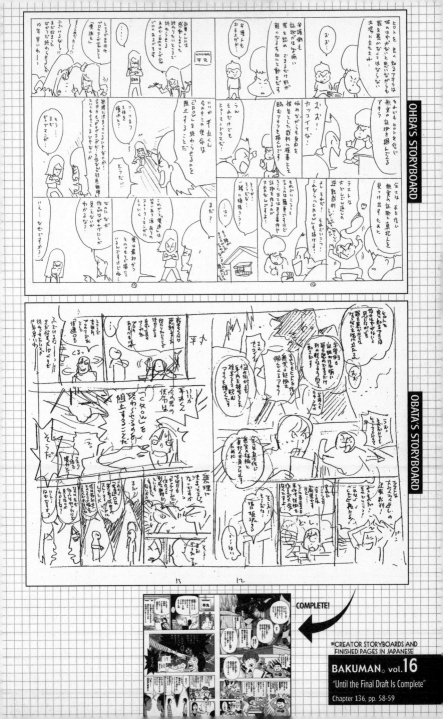

COMPLETE!

*CREATOR STORYBOARDS AND
FINISHED PAGES IN JAPANESE

BAKUMAN。vol.16
"Until the Final Draft Is Complete"
Chapter 136, pp. 58-59

THE EDITORS ARE STARTING TO GET FIDGETY TOO.

RIGHT...

THERE'S NO DOUBT ABOUT THAT.

THE MANGA THAT GETS FIRST PLACE IS THE BEST MANGA.

FIDGETY?

THE VETERAN EDITORS ARE ALL TALKING ABOUT WHICH WORK WILL BEAT *CROW* AND NOT ABOUT WHETHER YOU CAN BEAT CROW OR NOT. ALTHOUGH, I DO THINK THEY'RE TALKING ABOUT IT THAT WAY BECAUSE THEY HAVE THEIR FINGERS CROSSED...

...

WHAT...

THEY'RE ALL TALKING ABOUT WHICH SERIES WOULD BEAT *CROW* AND GET FIRST PLACE.

MIKATA'S JUSTICE?

...MIKATA'S JUSTICE!

B-BY THE WAY, WHICH IS THE OFFICE'S FAVORITE?

WHAT?

CURRENTLY, IT'S...

I-I SEE. I NEVER KNEW YOU HAD PUT THAT INTO THE CALCULATION AS WELL!

RIGHT! YOU TOTALLY GOT THIS!

THE TURNABOUT VERDICT IS IN THREE CHAPTERS, AND I'LL HAVE FRONT COLOR PAGES IN THAT ISSUE.

THIS IS GOING TO WORK, MR. MIURA ...

YOU RECEIVED SIXTH PLACE AGAIN.

...

N-NO!! MY DREAM OF BEING CALLED KAZUTAN IS FALLING OUT OF MY REACH...

YOU FELL FROM FIFTH TO SEVENTH PLACE...

HIRAMARU 平丸

BUT I WANT TO BE CALLED KAZUTAN.

AAAAAH! I CAN'T TAKE THIS ANY-MORE.

YES!

NAKAI, TAKE CARE OF HIM. I WANT YOU TO IMPROVE HIRAMARU'S ARTWORK EVEN MORE.

MUCH MUCH

FSH

YOUR RANK WILL GO UP AS SOON AS THE READERS GET USED TO IT.

PROB-ABLY...

DON'T WORRY. THE READERS ARE JUST SURPRISED AT HOW MUCH YOUR ARTWORK HAS IMPROVED. IN SOME WAYS, THIS IS PROOF THAT YOU'RE SUCCEEDING.

71

...

CROW, FIRST PLACE.

WE WENT UP A RANK!

PCP, THIRD PLACE.

THE FOLLOWING FRIDAY

...

MIKATA'S JUSTICE HAS FRONT COLOR PAGES IN THE ISSUE TWO WEEKS FROM NOW AND GIRI WILL HAVE FRONT COLOR PAGES A WEEK AFTER THAT. THOSE TWO MAY REALLY BEAT CROW...

WOW...

!

GIRI GOT SECOND PLACE. MIKATA'S JUSTICE GOT FOURTH PLACE.

THIS MEANS NIZUMA'S CROW... HAS RECEIVED FIRST PLACE FOR TEN WEEKS IN A ROW NOW.

THAT'S RIGHT.

NOT NECESSARILY.

?

PLUS TO EIJI MAYBE WE'RE JUST A BUNCH OF PEOPLE GETTING IN THE WAY OF CROW COMING TO AN END?

....!

YOU'RE RIGHT... IT'S FRUSTRATING THAT WE'VE ALREADY LET HIM GET THAT FAR.

BASED ON THE ORIGINAL DEAL BETWEEN JUST NIZUMA AND THE EDITOR IN CHIEF, CROW WOULD NOW START TO WRAP UP ITS STORY AND END IN ANOTHER TEN WEEKS...

75

I'M SO HAPPY TO HEAR THAT EVERYBODY IS GETTING MORE VOTES AND CATCHING UP WITH ME!

IS THAT SO!

VSH

KRBOOOM!

FSH

FSH

YOUR CONFIDENCE IS AMAZING AS ALWAYS...

IT WOULD BE NO FUN IF THEY DIDN'T.

FIGHTING THEM OFF AND FINISHING THE SERIES IN FIRST PLACE WILL BE THE PINNACLE OF AWESOMENESS!

THRILLING!

BOOOSH!

REALLY...

...

YUJIRO TOLD ME THAT BEFORE I CAME HERE AND SAID THAT NIZUMA SEEMED TO BE VERY LIVELY.

...

YES!

LET'S BEAT HIM!

I WANT TO KNOCK THE WIND OUT OF NIZUMA'S SAILS TOO.

76

BUT THAT WASN'T ENOUGH TO WIN MORE VOTES... DOES THAT MEAN COOL COLOR ILLUSTRATIONS AREN'T ENOUGH BY THEMSELVES...?

FUKUDA'S TWO-PAGE COLOR SPREAD WAS REALLY COOL AND WELL DRAWN...

...

PCP HASN'T CHANGED FROM LAST WEEK... AND EVEN GIRI COULDN'T MAKE IT...

GIRI, SECOND PLACE. PCP, THIRD PLACE.

RIGHT. I KIND OF FORCED THEM TO GIVE YOU THE COLOR PAGE, SO YOU DON'T HAVE MUCH TIME. THE LATEST I CAN WAIT FOR THE COLOR PAGE IS THE 8TH. THAT'S IN A WEEK.

THOSE RESULTS WILL COME OUT RIGHT BEFORE NIZUMA CREATES THE FINAL CHAPTER.

WAIT... ISSUE 34 IS...

SWEET!

AND PCP WILL GET CENTER COLOR IN ISSUE 34.

...

IF NO ONE HAS BEATEN CROW BY ISSUE 34, THAT WILL BE OUR LAST CHANCE OF SURPASSING IT.

...? YEAH, YOU COULD TELL HE SPENT A WHOLE MONTH ON IT.

THE ILLUSTRATION WAS AMAZING, WASN'T IT.

GIRI'S COLOR PAGES...

...

RIGHT?

...

I'M GONNA RACE THROUGH AT TOP GEAR!!

GIRI!

PCP HAS ONLY MANAGED TO GO UP TO THIRD PLACE... SO IT MAY BE DIFFICULT FOR US TO GET FIRST PLACE WITH JUST ONE COLOR PAGE IN THE MIDDLE OF THE MAGAZINE...

Front Color

Center Color

GIRI HAS BEEN IN SECOND PLACE RECENTLY BUT WAS STILL UNABLE TO GET AHEAD OF CROW EVEN WITH THREE COLOR PAGES AT THE FRONT OF THE MAGAZINE...

UMM... LIKE THINGS WILL COME JUMPING OUT IF YOU LOOK AT THE ILLUSTRATION WITH 3D GLASSES?

MAYBE WE CAN CREATE SOME KIND OF GIMMICK USING THE COLOR PAGE... SOMETHING ONLY PCP CAN DO.

BUT NO MATTER HOW MUCH TIME HE TOOK ON IT, I STILL THINK YOUR COLOR ILLUSTRATIONS ARE MORE ATTRACTIVE THAN FUKUDA'S.

THEN THE READERS ARE GOING TO NEED 3D GLASSES, AND THAT DOESN'T REALLY SEEM FAIR.

AND I CAN'T DRAW ILLUSTRATIONS IN 3D ANYWAY.

YES.

?

A GIMMICK THAT ONLY PCP CAN DO?

THAT'S NOT WHAT I MEAN...

HN?

82

BUT IT'D BE GREAT IF WE COULD DO THAT, RIGHT?

HMM...

I LIKE THE IDEA, BUT IT'S GOING TO BE DIFFICULT.

HOW CAN I PUT IT, I WANT THE STORY AND THE TITLE PAGE ILLUSTRATION TO BE CONNECTED...

...

I'LL THINK OF SOMETHING.

BUT YOU DON'T HAVE MUCH TIME. THE COLOR ILLUSTRATION IS DUE IN A WEEK AND DON'T FORGET TO DO YOUR STORYBOARDS TOO.

OKAY...

...

IT WOULD BE IMPRESSIVE IF YOU COULD REALLY CREATE A GIMMICK THAT CAN ONLY BE DONE IN PCP, BUT...

A COLOR ILLUSTRATION THAT'S CONNECTED TO THE ACTUAL STORY...

WHAT DO I HAVE TO DO TO BEAT CROW...?

AND WE'RE GOING TO HAVE A CENTER COLOR PAGE AT THE END OF THOSE FOUR WEEKS.

WE ONLY HAVE FOUR WEEKS LEFT...

...BUT WE COULDN'T THINK OF ANYTHING...

SORRY, KAYA... COULD YOU KEEP QUIET?

—SIGH

IT'LL BE IN COLOR SO YOU COULD DRAW A NIJI, AS IN A RAINBOW, AND SAY IT ACTUALLY MEANS "NIJI" FOR "2 O'CLOCK"! HOW'S THAT?

AND FROM THAT DAY ON, WE TRIED TO COME UP WITH CATCHY IDEAS FOR THE COLOR PAGE...

WHAT DO YOU THINK ABOUT THIS? I DON'T THINK YOU'LL LIKE IT, BUT...

MAYBE IT'LL HELP US COME UP WITH SOMETHING...

...

THE COLOR ILLUSTRATION IS DUE IN THREE DAYS. FORGET ABOUT DOING SOMETHING SPECIAL AND JUST DO AN ORDINARY COLOR PAGE.

YOU DON'T HAVE ANY MORE TIME.

FOUR DAYS LATER, JULY 5

THE TITLE PAGE ILLUSTRATION WILL BE A CLASS PHOTO, AND THAT WILL BE THE HINT SENT FROM SIGMA TO PCP.

WITH A CLUE LIKE, "ADD WHAT IS MISSING AND YOU WILL FIND OUT THE PERSON WHO IS THE KEY TO THIS MYSTERY" OR SOMETHING LIKE THAT...

AND THE PCP MEMBERS NOTICE THAT AOI ISN'T IN THE PHOTO.

SORRY...

THE SKY IS YELLOW? THAT'S WEIRD.

SO YOU REALIZE THAT MIDORI, AS IN GREEN, IS THE KEY PERSON TO SOLVE THIS MYSTERY.

...

AND THEN THIS PHOTO AND SKY WILL TURN GREEN...

AOI CAN ALSO MEAN "BLUE," SO YOU PLACE A BLUE PLASTIC FILM OVER THE PHOTO. AND WE'RE GOING TO PLACE A SCENE OF THAT IN THE MANGA AS WELL...

HAVING COLOR PAGES WILL ENABLE YOU TO WIN MORE VOTES COMPARED TO USUAL, BUT YOU STILL HAVE TO CONCENTRATE ON THE ACTUAL CONTENT OF THE MANGA.

IT'S GOING TO BE MEANINGLESS IF YOU GET TOO OBSESSED ABOUT INCLUDING A GIMMICK IN THE COLOR ILLUSTRATION AND END UP LOWERING THE QUALITY OF THE STORY.

AND MOST OF ALL, YOU NEED TO FEATURE THE MAIN CHARACTERS IN A TITLE PAGE LIKE THIS!!

WE'VE NEVER HAD A CHARACTER NAMED AOI APPEAR IN THE STORY BEFORE AND IT'S JUST WEIRD FOR THE SKY TO BE COLORED IN YELLOW.

NO!

GOT THAT?

TAKAGI, SIGMA IS A POPULAR CHARACTER, SO CREATE A STORY THAT WILL MAKE HIM LOOK COOLER!

MASHIRO, TURN IN A COLOR ILLUSTRATION FEATURING THE MAIN CHARACTERS IN THREE DAYS!

UNDERSTAND THAT THE COLOR ILLUSTRATION IS BASICALLY JUST A WAY TO PLEASE YOUR FANS.

YES, I UNDERSTAND. I'M SORRY...

I'M COUNTING ON YOU.

...

OKAY.

THANK YOU FOR COMING.

...

I'M NOT GOING TO GIVE UP UNTIL THE LAST MINUTE.

HE DIDN'T LIKE IT...

TMP...

KLAK

YEAH! LET'S THINK ABOUT IT UNTIL THE LAST MINUTE!

I JUST NEED A DAY TO DRAW THE COLOR ILLUSTRATION.

MR. HATTORI SAID IT WAS A GOOD IDEA IN THE BEGINNING TOO...

WHAT?!

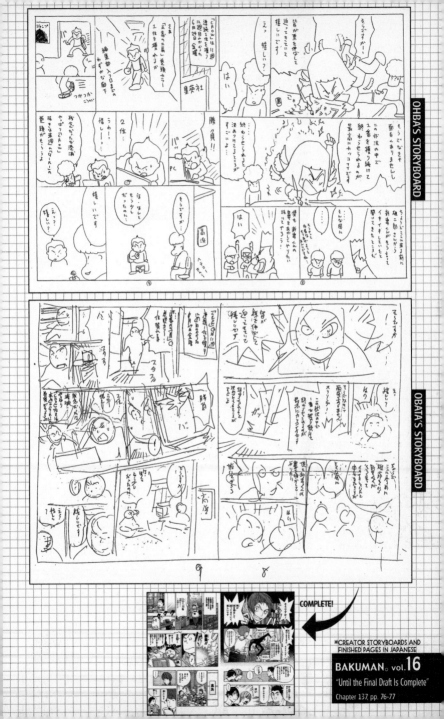

ONLY THREE WEEKS LEFT UNTIL ISSUE 34, WHICH WILL COME OUT ON JULY 25. UNLESS SOMEBODY STOPS CROW FROM GETTING FIRST PLACE BY THEN, EIJI WILL START CREATING THE FINAL CHAPTER AND BRING HIS SERIES TO A CLOSE.

SHWAAAA!

SKRT SKRT

KABOOOM!

CROW RECEIVED FIRST PLACE FOR THE FOUR-TEENTH WEEK IN A ROW.

CHAPTER 138 AGGRESSIVE AND IDEA

AND PCP WILL A HAVE A CENTER COLOR PAGE IN ISSUE 34.

SHF SHF

YEEAAAH! HERE'S THE STORY-BOARD!!

OOH!

VSH

IF WE CAN'T BEAT CROW WITH THE CHAPTERS FOR ISSUES 32 AND 33, WHICH WE'VE ALREADY TURNED IN, ISSUE 34 WILL BE OUR LAST CHANCE.

I CAN'T WAIT TO SEE HIS REACTION.

PHEW

HE SAID HE'S ON HIS WAY.

I'LL CALL HIM AND ASK IF HE CAN COME OVER.

LET'S NOT FAX THIS. I WANT MR. HATTORI TO READ IT HERE WITH US.

YOU COMPLETED IT JUST IN TIME.

FLIP

YOU GOT ME... MASHIRO, DO YOU HAVE A COPY OF THE COLOR ILLLUSTRATION YOU GAVE ME LAST WEEK?

YES.

...

TMP

IT'S GOOD. AND YOU'VE MADE GOOD USE OF THE COLOR AS WELL.

I NEVER REALIZED YOU HAD INCLUDED A GIMMICK LIKE THIS IN THE ILLUSTRATION ...

MASHIRO SENSEI, THE FINAL DRAFT THIS WEEK IS AMAZING.

YES! I'M DONE!

I SWEAR I'LL GET FIRST PLACE.

THANKS.

THIS IS DEFINITELY THE BEST WORK YOU'VE PRODUCED SO FAR.

RIGHT. I'M IMPRESSED WITH HOW YOU INCLUDED THE COLOR ILLUSTRATION INTO THE ACTUAL STORY SO MANY TIMES.

THE ARTWORK IS GREAT BUT SO IS THE STORY.

I'LL CALL MR. HATTORI TO TELL HIM THAT THE FINAL DRAFT WILL BE READY BY 9 O'CLOCK.

OKAY.

THIS IS A WONDERFUL FINAL DRAFT.

I CAN FEEL THE FLOW OF YOUR PEN ON IT.

: (NOTE: I SHALL BE WAITING FOR YOU AT THE DATE AND
: TIME YOU CAN FIGURE OUT FROM THIS PHOTOGRAPH.)

YEAH! THAT'S RIGHT!

GIRI CAN BEAT THEM AGAIN AFTER THAT.

I HATE TO ADMIT IT, BUT IF *GIRI* CAN'T BEAT MASTER NIZUMA, I WANT THIS TO WIN.

BAM

PHEW

SUCH A DEEP CHAPTER.

WELL DONE, ASHIROGI.

I KNEW IT. MUTO ASHIROGI IS STILL ABOVE ME... BOTH IN STORY AND ARTWORK...

SHF

TAKE A LOOK AT IT. IF YOU CAN CREATE SOMETHING LIKE THIS AND GET FIRST PLACE, YURITAN WILL BE ALL OVER YOU FOR SURE...

PCP REALLY IS GOOD.

CALM DOWN, HIRA-MARU.

FWUP

WHAT? WHAT? LEMME SEE.

AARGH! YOSHI-DA, WHY YOU!!

YOU IDIOT. DID YOU SERIOUSLY THINK *CAN'T FOOL ME* WOULD BE ABLE TO BEAT *CROW* FOR EVEN A SECOND? BUT AT LEAST I WAS ABLE TO GET YOU TO WORK HARD FOR ALMOST TEN WEEKS BY DANGLING THE KAZUTAN CARROT IN FRONT OF YOU.

HISSS

GSH

GSH

HONESTLY SPEAKING, I COULD CARE LESS ABOUT WHICH MANGA IS GOING TO END. ANYHOW, I DON'T HAVE A CHANCE OF BEING CALLED KAZUTAN ANYMORE, DO I?

PCP MIGHT JUST BEAT *CROW*.

AND IT MAKES ME EVEN HAPPIER THAT I WILL BE ABLE TO END MY SERIES BY HOLDING THEM OFF!

YES, THIS IS JUST LIKE ASHIROGI SENSEI.

ASHIROGI IS AMAZING TOO... THIS IS SUCH A GRAND BATTLE BETWEEN YOU TWO...

THEY INCLUDED THE GIMMICK FOR THE MYSTERY WITHIN THE COLOR ILLUSTRATION...

I FEEL SO MOVED AGAIN.

I'VE ALWAYS WANTED TO ASK YOU, BUT WHY ARE YOU SO HAPPY IF IT'S ASHIROGI?

...

IT WAS A FATEFUL MOMENT FOR BOTH OF US. THAT'S WHEN I REALIZED THAT WE NEVER WANTED TO LOSE TO EACH OTHER. THAT WE WOULD BECOME EACH OTHER'S BIGGEST RIVAL!

ESPECIALLY MASHIRO SENSEI WHO GLARED AT ME WITH FIERY EYES.

I WAS STRUCK BY LIGHTNING THE FIRST TIME I MET ASHIROGI SENSEI AT THE EDITORIAL DEPARTMENT.

THANK YOU VERY MUCH.

IT'S EVEN BETTER READING IT IN THE ACTUAL MAGAZINE.

WELCOME, MEMBERS OF PCP!

AND I LIKE HOW THE CHAPTER ENDS WITH A "SO IS SIGMA FINALLY GOING TO APPEAR?!" CLIFFHANGER.

FWOOSH FWOOSH

!!

FW

OOSH

...

ISSUE 34 WILL PROBABLY BE THE LAST CHANCE FOR EVERYBODY.

CROW RECEIVED FIRST PLACE IN ISSUE 32 ONCE AGAIN...

IS THIS GOING TO END AS A HISTORICAL MOMENT LIKE YUJIRO SAID...?

YEAH...

CROW HAS SO MUCH MOMENTUM RIGHT NOW THAT I DON'T THINK ANYBODY CAN STOP IT.

MURMUR

WE STILL HAVE PCP WITH THE CENTER COLOR PAGE.

MURMUR

IT'S FINALLY TIME.

ONE MORE WEEK.

AND AS MR. HATTORI SUSPECTED, CROW GOT FIRST PLACE IN ISSUE 33 AS WELL.

...

...

VEEEN————

STARING AT THE PHONE ISN'T GOING TO SPEED UP THE FINAL REPORT PROCESS, YOU KNOW.

...

LOOKS LIKE IT DID HELP.

WJ Mr. Hattori

FRIDAY, JULY 29. THE DAY FOR THE FINAL REPORT FOR ISSUE 34 TO BE REVEALED.

IF NONE OF US ARE ABLE TO STOP CROW FROM GETTING FIRST PLACE IN ISSUE 34, EIJI WILL START WORKING ON MAKING THE NEXT CHAPTER THE FINAL CHAPTER OF THE SERIES.

BNNNNN

BNNNN

SKRRR

BNNNN

B

SKRRR

CHAPTER 139
FINAL CHAPTER AND COMMENT

VSH

YES, TAKAGI SPEAKING!

TIED...?

SECOND PLACE...

TIED FOR SECOND PLACE?

PCP TIED FOR SECOND PLACE.

BAM

WHAT ABOUT CROW?

YOU DID REALLY WELL. THIS IS THE BEST RANK YOU'VE RECEIVED, APART FROM THE FIRST CHAPTER OF THE SERIES.

....!

A SEVENTEEN-VOTE GAP WITH CROW, WHICH GOT FIRST PLACE...

IT WAS ONLY A TWO-VOTE DIFFERENCE IN THE EARLY RESULTS, SO I DID HAVE MY FINGERS CROSSED, BUT...

GIRI WAS RANKED THIRD PLACE IN THE EARLY RESULTS, BUT THE EXCITING STORY ABOUT GIRI WINNING THE RACE USING HIS NEW RIDING TECHNIQUE MUST HAVE BEEN POPULAR.

CROW, 420 VOTES. PCP AND GIRI BOTH GOT 403 VOTES.

110

WE'VE JUST BEEN GIVEN THE GO-AHEAD TO INCLUDE THE WORDS "FINAL CHAPTER" ON THE COVER OF *JUMP* AND THE CHAPTER TITLE PAGE OF *CROW*.

RIGHT... IT WILL END IN THREE WEEKS WITH FRONT COLOR PAGES.

THAT MEANS *CROW* WILL...

THANK YOU, BUT...

IT HASN'T ENDED... SUMMER'S JUST STARTED...

OUR SUMMER HAS ENDED... THAT'S WHAT IT FEELS LIKE.

SIGH~~~~...

FWUM

P...

BANNNN

BANNNN

AND THAT'S WHY IT'S EVEN MORE FRUS-TRATING...

YEAH... IT IS COOL...

HE CONTINUED TO GET FIRST PLACE AND WILL END HIS SERIES WITH FRONT COLOR PAGES. THAT'S SO COOL...

EIJI SURE IS AMAZING...

THAT'S WHAT WE TOLD HIM THE FIRST TIME WE MET...

"PLEASE KEEP YOUR SERIES RUNNING, WE'LL CATCH UP WITH YOU."

I-IT'S NOT LIKE NIZUMA IS GOING TO QUIT BEING A MANGA ARTIST, RIGHT?

YEAH... BUT I FEEL LIKE WE'VE BEEN TOTALLY DEFEATED...

NAH. +NATURAL MAYBE, BUT WE HAVEN'T BEEN ABLE TO CATCH UP WITH CROW. THE ONLY TIME WE BEAT IT WAS WITH THE FIRST CHAPTER OF PCP...

BASICALLY, EIJI'S MANGA ARE BETTER WHEN HE CREATES THEM ON HIS OWN... IT WAS TWO OF US AGAINST HIM ALONE, BUT WE WERE STILL NO MATCH FOR HIM...

BUT I THINK YOU'RE AS GOOD AS HAVING CAUGHT UP WITH HIM.

AND NOW, CROW WILL END BEFORE WE COULD ACCOMPLISH IT... AND IT'S NOT BECAUSE IT WAS CANCELED EITHER. HE ENDED IT IN THE MOST PERFECT WAY POSSIBLE.

EIJI WAS WAITING FOR US WITH HIS SERIES. WE GOT OUR OWN SERIES TOO, BUT WE COULDN'T CATCH UP TO HIM...

SIGH

SIGH

HE'S TELLING THE STORY WITH ART ALONE...

THERE'S NO DIALOGUE!

YOU'VE FIGURED SOMETHING OUT, HAVEN'T YOU?

YEAH. THANKS.

AND, IT'S NOT JUST THAT WE WERE NO MATCH FOR HIM...

IF EIJI HADN'T BEEN AROUND, WE WOULD NEVER HAVE BEEN ABLE TO COME THIS FAR AS MANGA CREATORS...

MY RIVAL IS MUTO ASHIROGI SENSEI.

URRGH

THANK
YOU.

WHAT AN
AWESOME
ENDING.

T
M
P

AND ON
AUGUST 9
THE
SAMPLE
COPIES OF
ISSUE 38
WITH THE
FINAL
CHAPTER
OF CROW
WERE
PRINTED.

SENSEI?

NIZUMA
SENSEI...

MAYBE I FEEL
THIS WAY EVEN
MORE BECAUSE
YOU WERE ABLE TO
END THE SERIES
LIKE THIS, BUT...

V
I
P

THANK
YOU
VERY
MUCH
FOR
YOUR
HARD
WORK
!!

IT HAS
BEEN AN
HONOR TO
BE YOUR
EDITOR
FOR
CROW FROM
START TO
FINISH.

SP

CROW ENDS!!

IS THAT
SO?

AND...

CROW ENDS!

BUT YOU SHOULD HAVE MORE TIME TO RELAX THAN BEFORE.

YOU STILL HAVE +NATURAL SO I CAN'T TELL YOU TO TAKE SOME TIME OFF...

HE SOUNDS LIKE HE'S TOTALLY MOVED ON TO SOMETHING ELSE.

...

WUMP

SFF SFF

THANK YOU VERY MUCH TOO.

HUH? THEN WHAT IS IT?

IS THAT A NEW CHARACTER FOR +NATURAL? NICE!

HM?

BUT I'VE ONLY INTRODUCED PT(PLATINUM) AND AG(SILVER) IN THE STORY SO FAR.

I HAVEN'T GIVEN IT A TITLE YET BUT IT'S A HERO MANGA USING CHEMICAL SYMBOLS.

THIS ISN'T +NATURAL.

SFF SFF

C-CAN I TAKE A LOOK AT IT?!

Y-YOU'RE ALREADY WORKING ON A NEW SERIES ?!

RUSTLE

I'M JUST DRAWING BECAUSE I FEEL UNCOMFORTABLE IF I'M NOT DRAWING.

SFF SFF

THAT MEANS HE'S ALREADY COMPLETED AROUND FOUR CHAPTERS, EVEN IF THE FIRST CHAPTER IS FIFTY PAGES LONG...

A HUNDRED?!

I THINK I'VE DRAWN AROUND A HUNDRED PAGES BEFORE THAT.

OOH, YOU'RE SO NOISY.

THIS IS ALREADY IN THE MIDST OF THE STORY, RIGHT?

I'M NOT DRAWING THIS FOR SERIALIZATION, SO I DON'T NEED TO CHECK.

HAVE YOU CHECKED ON THAT, NIZUMA?

MAYBE NOT AS MUCH AS CONSTELLATIONS AND THE ORIENTAL ZODIAC, BUT...

BUT I HAVE A FEELING THAT SOMEBODY'S ALREADY DONE A MANGA ABOUT HEROES WITH THE TABLE OF ELEMENTS...

...AS CROW....!

AND IT'S AS GOOD...

I DON'T KNOW, BUT MAYBE AROUND THIRTY VOLUMES' WORTH IN TERMS OF *JUMP* GRAPHIC NOVELS...

AND FULL-LENGTH? HOW LONG IS THAT?!

THE SPACE COCKROACH?! WHAT'S THAT?!

IF YOU WANT TO READ SOMETHING NO ONE HAS EVER SEEN BEFORE, I RECOMMEND THE FULL-LENGTH MANGA ABOUT THE SPACE COCKROACH.

HOLD ON, COULD YOU SHOW ME ALL THE WORK YOU HAVEN'T SHOWN ME BEFORE?!

SWSH

SWSH

SWSH

PHEW— BOOOM

IN THE SPARE TIME I HAD WHILE WORKING ON *CROW* AND *+NATURAL*.

WHEN IN THE WORLD DID YOU CREATE ALL OF THIS?!

MOST PEOPLE DON'T HAVE ANY SPARE TIME. IN FACT, THEY USUALLY DON'T HAVE ENOUGH TIME...!

FWUMP

OR EVEN BETTER....!

UNBELIEVABLE... AND THEY'RE ALL AS GOOD AS *CROW* AS WELL.

WSH

I HAD EVEN MORE TIME WHEN I WAS ONLY DOING *CROW*, OF COURSE.

SHF SHF SHF

...

THAT'S WHAT HE SAID, BUT...

HAVE HIM CREATE A NEW SERIES AS SOON AS POSSIBLE.

THE EDITOR IN CHIEF...

118

IT'LL PROBABLY BE BETTER TO LET HIM DO AS HE FEELS RATHER THAN SPECIFYING WHAT HE SHOULD CREATE... NO NEED TO RUSH... AT THIS RATE... NIZUMA WILL BE ABLE TO CREATE SOMETHING BETTER THAN CROW... NO...

I DON'T HAVE TO TELL HIM TO CREATE SOMETHING NEW...

I SEE. EVEN THOUGH I TOLD NIZUMA TO TAKE SOME TIME OFF, HE'LL STILL CONTINUE TO DRAW MANGA. HE JUST WANTS TO CONTINUE DRAWING MANGA.

RIGHT... CROW WAS POPULAR, BUT IT WAS STILL A SERIES THAT ONLY RECEIVED FIRST PLACE FOR TWENTY WEEKS IN A ROW IN JUMP...

HE HAS THE POTENTIAL TO CREATE THE GREATEST MASTERPIECE IN JUMP HISTORY... OR EVEN THE GREATEST THING EVER CREATED; PERIOD.

OOOH?! I CAN GO?!

I-I SEE... IT'LL PROBABLY BE DIFFICULT TO GO SEE ALL OF THOSE, BUT THE COMPANY IS WILLING TO PAY FOR A RESEARCH TRIP AS A WAY TO THANK YOU FOR YOUR HARD WORK AND SO YOU CAN BROADEN YOUR HORIZONS.

I WANT HIM TO GATHER MORE IDEAS AND KNOWLEDGE FOR NOW...

MR. YUJIRO, YOU'VE SUDDENLY BECOME SO QUIET. IS ANYTHING THE MATTER?

I WANT TO SEE THE LOUVRE MUSEUM, THE PYRAMIDS AND THE AURORA BOREALIS.

I KNOW. NIZUMA, IS THERE ANYWHERE YOU'D LIKE TO GO? ANY PLACE IN THE WORLD IS FINE.

YES.

N-NO. ALL THE FINAL DRAFTS HERE ARE NOT SOMETHING YOU CREATED FOR A SERIES, RIGHT?

THEY ALL WROTE "THANK YOU AND NICE WORK" IN THE COMMENTS.

HM? YEAH, THAT'S PRETTY COMMON THESE DAYS.

!

ました。いや——あんなに賞いっぱなしなってそうないです。面白かった～〈雖隹〉

Mikata's Justice
Shoyo Takahama
Nizuma Sensei, thank you very much for your hard work on *Crow*. I'm going to continue to work hard so I can catch up with you. (Shoyo)

47

God Given
Ko Aoki
Nizuma Sensei, nice work on *Crow*. Good luck on *+Natural*! (Ko)

67

Can't Fool Me
Kazuya Hiramaru
I was so moved by the way you ended *Crow*! I want to end my series in a cool way like you as soon as I can! (Kazuya)

85

PCP -Perfect Crime Party-
Muto Ashirogi

I want to end my series in a cool way... as soon as I can! (Kazuya)

PCP -Perfect Crime Party-
Muto Ashirogi
Thank you very much for your hard work on *Crow*, Nizuma Sensei. I am grateful to you for accepting my challenge at the end. (Muto)

105

YOU DON'T HAVE TO GO THAT FAR...

I GUESS I SHOULD GO AND THANK THE PEOPLE WHO WROTE COMMENTS TO ME.

...

BUT THE READERS WILL PROBABLY HAVE NO IDEA WHAT THEY'RE TALKING ABOUT.

ASHIROGI ARE EARNEST GUYS...

HE'S TALKING ABOUT HOW YOU CHANGED FROM GETTING FIRST PLACE FOR TEN WEEKS IN A ROW TO GETTING FIRST PLACE UNTIL RIGHT BEFORE THE FINAL CHAPTER, ISN'T HE?

I CAME TO TELL YOU THAT.

BOW

THE HONOR IS ALL MINE. IT LIT A FIRE INSIDE ME AND I WAS ABLE TO CREATE SOMETHING EVEN BETTER.

"I AM GRATEFUL TO YOU FOR ACCEPTING MY CHALLENGE AT THE END"...

GR IN

TAKAGI ONCE SAID THAT MAYBE WE'RE JUST A BUNCH OF PEOPLE GETTING IN THE WAY OF CROW COMING TO AN END.

...

I... WAS THE ONE WHO SAID WE SHOULD CHALLENGE YOU.

I SEE...

WUMP

SEE YA!

SWIP

THAT...

NO. NOT AT ALL.

WE WEREN'T GETTING IN YOUR WAY, WERE WE?

BUT THAT'S NOT TRUE, IS IT?

COMPLETE!

※CREATOR STORYBOARDS AND
FINISHED PAGES IN JAPANESE

BAKUMAN。 vol.16
"Until the Final Draft Is Complete"
Chapter 139, pp. 126-127

THAT BASICALLY MEANS IT'LL BE THE BEST MANGA IN THE WORLD.

OKAY, BUT WHAT IS THE BEST MANGA THAT HAS EVER COME INTO EXISTENCE ANYWAY?

BUT EIJI SAID "I'LL GET FIRST PLACE IN *JUMP*" AND MANAGED TO CONTINUE GETTING FIRST PLACE, SO HE MAY BE ABLE TO DO IT.

...BUT HE'S NOT THE KIND OF GUY WHO CAN CREATE A GOOD PIECE OF WORK WHILE THINKING ABOUT THAT, IS HE?

EIJI SAID HIS NEXT MANGA IS GOING TO BE THE BEST MANGA OF ALL TIME...

CHAPTER 140
LIMIT AND PHOENIX

WHAT...? THE GREATEST MANGA THAT HAS EVER COME INTO EXISTENCE?

SHOOT, I NEED TO WORK ON MY INKING.

COME ON, THE ASSISTANTS ARE REALLY HERE THIS TIME.

CLOMP CLOMP

CLOMP CLOMP

IF I HAD TO CHOOSE ONE, IT WOULD BE TEZUKA SENSEI'S *PHOENIX*.

THE GREATEST MANGA AND MY FAVORITE MANGA ARE DIFFERENT, BUT...

THE ROSE OF VERSAILLES OR GLASS MASK.

MINE IS A SHOJO MANGA.

...SLAM DUNK!!

I'D DEFINITELY SAY...

I READ THAT HERE IN THIS STUDIO WHEN I WAS LITTLE AND I CAN STILL REMEMBER HOW I COULDN'T FALL ASLEEP THAT NIGHT...

BAREFOOT GEN...

THAT'S MY FAVORITE MANGA... BUT IF WE'RE TALKING ABOUT THE GREATEST MANGA, I THINK I'D GO WITH SOMETHING ELSE TOO.

SAIKO, YOURS IS TOMORROW'S JOE, RIGHT?

YOU CAN TELL A PERSON'S PERSONALITY BASED ON WHAT KIND OF MANGA THEY LIKE.

I NEED TO DO THAT TOO.

YOU GUYS HAVE DONE YOUR RESEARCH... WELL, READ SO MANY TYPES OF MANGA.

THAT'S A MANGA THAT MUST BE PASSED DOWN FROM GENERATION TO GENERATION.

A CLASSIC!

I GUESS THAT'S TRUE. BUT YOU CAN'T HELP THAT PEOPLE WILL RANK THINGS USING SALES NUMBERS OR OTHER FACTORS ...

BUT RECENTLY I'VE SEEN A LOT OF RANKINGS IN MAGAZINES AND WHATNOT THAT I'M NOT TOO SURE ABOUT. EVERY MANGA CREATOR HAS PUT THEIR HEART AND SOUL IN THEIR WORK, AFTER ALL.

I THINK IT'S A VERY GOOD THING FOR US TO TALK ABOUT OUR FAVORITE MANGA AND WHICH ARE CLASSICS...

MY NEXT MANGA ISN'T GOING TO BE THE BEST IN JUMP. IT WILL BE THE BEST MANGA THAT HAS EVER COME INTO EXISTENCE...

IS THAT WHAT EIJI IS TRYING TO DO ...?

I WANT TO CREATE SOMETHING THAT PEOPLE WILL CONSIDER A CLASSIC NO MATTER HOW OLD IT BECOMES, AND NOT SOMETHING THAT'S JUST PANDERING FOR CURRENT POPULARITY...

BUT TALKING ABOUT THIS IS STARTING TO MAKE ME A LITTLE SAD ABOUT OUR WORK...

...

131

IF MR. MIURA ISN'T SERIOUS ABOUT THE SERIES, THEN I'LL PERSONALLY TALK TO NIZUMA MYSELF...

...

KAK KAK

KAK KAK

101 岩瀬 IWASE

KRSHAA

COULD YOU PLEASE DO SOMETHING ABOUT THE SERIES SO IT WILL BECOME MORE POPULAR...?

BUT WHAT AM I GOING TO SAY TO HIM?

RIGHT... I HAVE TO DO IT ALONE... AND IF IT DOESN'T WORK OUT... I'LL...

ALONE...

I COULD NEVER SAY THAT... I HAVE TO DO SOMETHING ABOUT IT MYSELF...

RRR

THAT'S RIGHT. WE'RE NOT STARTING A SECOND ARC OF THE SERIES NEXT WEEK.

NO... WE TALKED ABOUT IT WITH NIZUMA SENSEI AND CAME TO THE DECISION THAT IT WOULD BE BEST FOR THE SERIES TO END IT HERE...

MONDAY, AUGUST 22. ISSUE 38 WITH THE FINAL CHAPER OF CROW IS PUBLISHED.

RRR

THE SERIES DIDN'T END BECAUSE NIZUMA SENSEI HAS A NEW SERIES COMING UP...

RRR

RRR

142

...

YO!

THEN YOU WOULDN'T HAVE TO FRET OVER STUFF ALONE.

EVERY-BODY'S GONNA WELCOME YOU.

STOP BEING STUBBORN AND BECOME A MEMBER OF TEAM FUKUDA.

I'M SORRY I DIDN'T REALIZE THAT YOU WERE IN TROUBLE WHEN YOU CALLED ME.

...

BUT WE'VE JUST LOST A POWERFUL RIVAL IN *CROW* AND I DON'T WANT TO LOSE MY BIGGEST MANGA WRITER RIVAL TOO...

I'M NOT GOING TO STOP YOU IF YOU REALLY WANT TO QUIT.

GO ON.

...

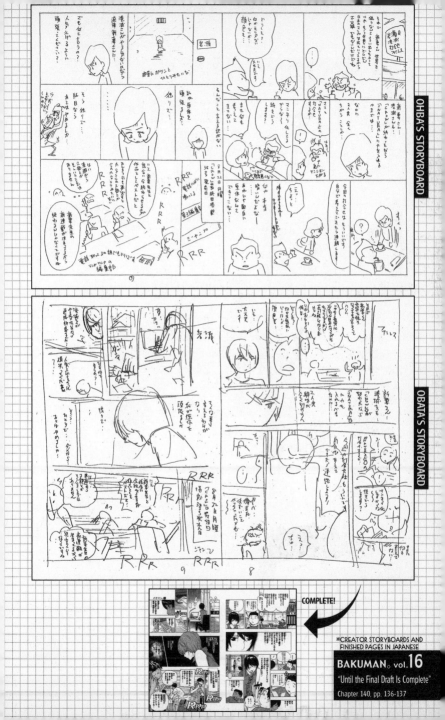

COMPLETE!

*CREATOR STORYBOARDS AND
FINISHED PAGES IN JAPANESE

BAKUMAN。vol.16
"Until the Final Draft Is Complete"
Chapter 140, pp. 136-137

MIURA, YOU HAVE A CALL FROM THE FRONT DESK. BOOTH NUMBER 2.

OH, RIGHT.

```
Editor in Chief
      ↑
Deputy Editor in Chief
      ↑
Captain
```

+NATURAL *ISN'T A SERIES I STARTED MYSELF, BUT IT'S BEGINNING TO GET BACK ON ITS FEET AGAIN. AND THE TV DRAMA FOR MIKATA'S JUSTICE WILL START ON OCTOBER 8. IF THAT BECOMES A BIG HIT, I'LL PROBABLY JUST NEED TO RAISE ONE MORE HOT ROOKIE AND...*

CHAPTER 14 AGE AND ACHIEVEMENT

YOU SEEM REALLY GUNG-HO THESE DAYS.

DASH

I'M GOING DOWN TO CHECK OUT A SUBMISSION!

BOOTH NUMBER 2? PLEASE TELL HIM I'LL BE THERE RIGHT AWAY.

YES! AZUMA DOES HAVE AN APPOINTMENT WITH ME.

!

BOOTH NUMBER 2 IS...

2

TMP TMP TMP

SORRY TO KEEP YOU WAITING. I'M MIURA OF *WEEKLY JUMP.*

LOOKING FOR TALENTED ROOKIES THROUGH CONTEST SUBMISSIONS IS GOOD, BUT THE BEST WAY IS TO HAVE THEM BRING US THEIR WORK LIKE THIS.

BIP BIP

THERE REALLY AREN'T THAT MANY GOOD EDITORS THERE ANYWAY; SO I THOUGHT HE MIGHT BE BARELY OKAY... OKAY THEN, PLEASE CALL THE EDITORIAL OFFICE AGAIN.

RIGHT...

HE WAS AN UNPLEASANT GUY, SO I LEFT SHUEISHA WITHOUT SHOWING HIM THE WORK.

IT'S JUST AS YOU SAID. THAT EDITOR NAMED MIURA IS NO GOOD.

TOMORROW AT 4...

CHIK

OF COURSE. YOU'RE ALWAYS WELCOME.

YOU WANT TO BRING YOUR WORK IN?

WEEKLY SHONEN JUMP EDITORIAL OFFICE.

BIP

I DON'T HAVE TIME TODAY...

I'M GOING DOWN TO ASHIROGI'S STUDIO TO PICK UP THE FINAL DRAFT AND HAVE A MEETING.

SIGH...

CAN YOU COME DOWN AT 4 TOMORROW? YES... YES... MR. AZUMA.

RRR

SHUP

MY NAME IS AKIRA HATTORI.

I LIKE HOW THE PCP MEMBERS ARE UNWITTINGLY BEING TRAINED BY SIGMA.

GOOD. ANOTHER STRONG CHAPTER.

WE ALWAYS NEED SOME KIND OF RIVAL CHARACTER.

T*m*p

YES.

NEXT WORK?

SHUJIN!

TO TELL YOU THE TRUTH, SIGMA IS ALSO MEANT TO BE A TEST FOR OUR NEXT WORK.

I COULD NEVER COME UP WITH A CHARACTER LIKE THIS.

AND IT'S ALSO CLEVER HOW SIGMA IS DRAWN AS AN ENEMY TO PCP.

SHFF

WE'RE THINKING ABOUT A CULT-HIT MAIN-STREAM BATTLE MANGA NEXT.

OKAY. GO AHEAD.

WE'RE STILL WORKING ON *PCP*, YOU KNOW...

NO, I THINK WE SHOULD TELL MR. HATTORI ABOUT IT.

BUT THE MAIN CHARACTER ISN'T GOING TO BE JUST. HE'LL BE AN EVIL DARK HERO.

HEY, HEY. THAT'S TOTALLY MAINSTREAM.

YES. WE'LL HAVE A COOL-LOOKING MAIN CHARACTER, WHO'D BE POPULAR WITH THE READERS, HAVE BATTLES...

A CULT-HIT MAINSTREAM BATTLE MANGA...?

BUT THAT IS GOING TO BE DIFFICULT, YOU KNOW. THERE'S A GOOD CHANCE OF IT NOT GETTING APPROVED FOR *JUMP* IF THIS CHARACTER IS DOWNRIGHT EVIL.

...

I GUESS THAT WOULD MAKE IT NON-MAINSTREAM IN TERMS OF *WEEKLY SHONEN JUMP*.

A DARK HERO, HUH...?

LIKE WE TOLD YOU BEFORE, OUR DREAM IS TO HAVE OUR WORK ANIMATED.

....!

AND IT COULD MAKE IT HARDER TO GET AN ANIME.

THE NEXT DAY

2

...

I FIND IT HARD TO BELIEVE THAT HE'D BE ABLE TO KEEP UP WITH WHAT SHONEN JUMP NEEDS... THIS ISN'T AN EASY JOB...

I'VE NEVER SEEN SUCH AN ELDERLY PERSON BRING HIS WORK IN...

SORRY TO KEEP YOU WAITING. I'M HATTORI OF WEEKLY JUMP.

KLAK

SWP

AT LEAST HE'S BETTER THAN MIURA FROM YESTERDAY SINCE HE DIDN'T FROWN.

THANK YOU.

WELL THEN, MAY I TAKE A LOOK AT YOUR WORK PLEASE?

...

MUST I WRITE MY AGE?

PLEASE FILL IN THIS SURVEY WHILE I'M LOOKING AT YOUR WORK.

I SAID SURVEY, BUT IT'S VERY SIMPLE AND YOU JUST NEED TO WRITE YOUR ADDRESS, AGE, NAME, A BRIEF SUMMARY OF YOUR CAREER, AND TITLES OF MANGA YOU LIKE.

SHP

Date:
Name:
Gender:
Date of Birth / Age:
Month Day Year

I DON'T THINK AGE MATTERS IF YOU ARE ABLE TO CREATE SOMETHING THAT THE READERS OF *JUMP* WILL LIKE.

BUT HAVING A SERIES IN A WEEKLY MAGAZINE REQUIRES A LOT OF PHYSICAL STAMINA AND MENTAL STRENGTH, SO I DO THINK IT WOULD HELP TO BE YOUNG IN THAT RESPECT...

DO YOU THINK AGE HAS ANYTHING TO DO WITH DRAWING MANGA?

YOU MUST.

...

SP.

THEN I'LL FILL IN THE SURVEY HONESTLY.

I SEE. I UNDER-STAND.

BUT... PANTY FLASH FIGHT...? THE TITLE IS RATHER OUT OF DATE AND SO'S HIS STYLE...

HIS ARTWORK IS EXCELLENT.

Title
Panty Flash Fight

Pretty Soldier No. 9
Momoko Magokoro
Age 18
Level 68011
TD Item: Double Speed

Panty Try Arena!

Welcome to the P.T.A!!

This evening, we're gonna have the semi-finals which will decide the eight fighters who will move their way up to the finals at the end of this month!!

HE OBVIOUSLY KNOWS HIS BASICS!

THEY AREN'T WEARING SOMETHING THAT CAN BE SEEN UNDERNEATH THEIR SKIRTS. THEY'RE WEARING THE VERY PANTIES THEY WERE WEARING ON THE DAY THEY WERE SCOUTED! IN OTHER WORDS, THEY'RE WEARING THEIR OWN REAL PANTIES!

PRETTY GIRLS FROM ALL OVER THE COUNTRY ARE HAVING SERIOUS PANTY FLASH BATTLES IN MINISKIRTS...

TH-THIS IS SO SILLY...

BUT THE MAIN CHARACTER IS MOMOKO'S YOUNGER BROTHER, SO THE STORY IS WRITTEN FROM THE POINT OF VIEW OF A BOY.

THE SETTING OF THE STORY IS INTRODUCED IN THE FIRST FOUR PAGES, AND STARTING FROM THE FIFTH PAGE, WE GET TO SEE FLASHBACKS OF WHY SHE ENDED UP HERE AND HOW SHE TRAINED...

HE ALSO KNOWS WHAT JUMP IS LOOKING FOR...

EACH FEMALE FIGHTER HAS ONE SPECIAL ABILITY... AND WILL FACE EACH ANOTHER IN A TOURNAMENT!

TH-THIS IS GOOD... TH-THIS IS...

AND MOST OF ALL, IT IS STILL A SERIOUS BATTLE.

...AND HE'S ALSO DRAWN THE GIRLS BEING SELF-CONSCIOUS ABOUT NOT WANTING TO SHOW THEIR PANTIES IN DETAIL!

HE HAS EXPLAINED THE REASONS AND RESPONSIBILITIES FOR EACH OF THE GIRLS TO ENTER THIS TOURNAMENT...

VIP

NOW THIS IS A CULT-HIT MAINSTREAM BATTLE MANGA!

MR. AZUMA, THIS IS INCREDIBLY GOOD!

B

KLAK

WE COULD CREATE OTHER MEDIA FRANCHISES WITH IT. AS A MATTER OF FACT, WE SHOULD DO THAT FROM THE START!

COSTUMES THAT WILL MAKE PEOPLE WANT TO COSPLAY.

ANIME! TV DRAMA!

GAMES!

LOTS OF CUTE GIRLS AND PANTY SHOTS!

TRADING CARDS! ACTION FIGURES!

BUT IT'S WONDERFUL BECAUSE THE MANGA IS A SERIOUS BATTLE MANGA AND NOT JUST A PANTY SHOT MANGA!!

NO.

YOU SWEAR TO GOD?

YES.

YOU HAVEN'T TAKEN THIS TO OTHER PUBLISHERS OR SHOWN IT TO OTHER PEOPLE, HAVE YOU?

TH-THANK YOU VERY MUCH.

YOU'RE A TRUE PROFESSIONAL TO HAVE BEEN ABLE TO EXPAND A SIMPLE IDEA LIKE THAT AND CREATE SUCH A GOOD MANGA!

THAT'S ALL THERE IS TO IT BUT...

I-IT'S GREAT... YOU LOSE IF YOU SHOW YOUR PANTIES!

O-OF COURSE. BUT...

I WOULD LIKE TO SHOW THIS TO MY BOSSES AND HAVE IT PLACED IN THE MAGAZINE AS A ONE-SHOT. IS THAT OKAY?

I'LL JUST HAVE TO REVISE THIS OUT-OF-DATE TITLE AND DIALOGUE AND... NO, MAYBE I SHOULD LEAVE THE TITLE AS *PANTY FLASH FIGHT* SINCE IT DOES HAVE A LOT OF IMPACT...

WE SHOULD STILL HAVE AN OPEN SLOT FOR A ONE-SHOT.

EVEN IF SOMEONE LIKE ME BRINGS THEIR WORK IN AS A ROOKIE, THE EDITORIAL DEPARTMENT WILL USUALLY JUST REJECT IT IMMEDIATELY.

JUMP FOCUSES ON CULTIVATING YOUNG MANGA CREATORS BY PROVIDING THEM WITH THE CHANCE OF HAVING A SERIES.

IN THAT CASE, I SHOULD LIE ABOUT MY AGE, SHOULDN'T I?

THEN DO YOU SERIOUSLY THINK THAT A FIFTY-YEAR-OLD MAN LIKE ME, WHO HAS NEVER EVEN HAD A ONE-SHOT PLACED IN *JUMP*, CAN REALLY GET A SERIES?

AS FOR THE POTENTIAL OF IMPROVING, I FEEL THAT THERE ARE PEOPLE WHO HAVE A CHANCE OF IMPROVING NO MATTER HOW OLD THEY ARE.

BUT THE MOST IMPORTANT THING IS THE QUALITY OF THE WORK AND HOW PASSIONATE YOU ARE ABOUT MANGA. AGE IS INSIGNIFICANT.

IF SOMEONE AROUND TWENTY YEARS OLD AND SOMEONE AROUND FORTY OR FIFTY BROUGHT THEIR WORK IN, AND IF THOSE WORKS HAPPENED TO BE AROUND THE SAME LEVEL, WE'D PROBABLY CHOOSE THE YOUNGER PERSON SINCE THEY HAVE MORE POTENTIAL TO IMPROVE... AND I DO ADMIT THAT THERE ARE HARDHEADED EDITORS WHO WILL PRETTY MUCH TURN YOU DOWN THE MOMENT THEY SEE YOU.

...

THAT WAS MR. AZUMA... WHAT IS HE DOING AT SHUEISHA AFTER ALL THIS TIME...?

LIKE I HEARD, HE DOES HAVE A GOOD EYE FOR MANGA...

AKIRA HATTORI! ...

YOU DID IT, SENPAI!

YOU HIT THE JACKPOT WITH THIS ONE!

RIGHT. THIS IS THE KIND OF MANGA I WANTED TO SEE IN JUMP.

RIGHT!

THIS ISN'T SILLY AT ALL. IT'S A MASTERPIECE!!

MURMUR

MURMUR

MURMUR

nen Jump

Jump SQ

V Square

SHF

SHF

IT'S REALLY GOOD.

WE STILL HAVE AN OPEN SLOT FOR A ONE-SHOT IN THE FALL, DON'T WE?

MR. HEISHI, PLEASE TAKE A LOOK AT THIS!

WHAT'S WITH ALL THE NOISE?

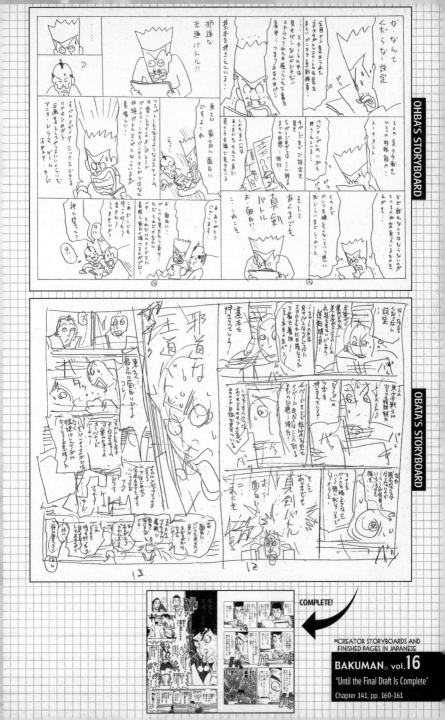

COMPLETE!

※CREATOR STORYBOARDS AND
FINISHED PAGES IN JAPANESE

BAKUMAN。vol.16
"Until the Final Draft Is Complete"
Chapter 141, pp. 160-161

WHY'D HE REJECT THAT SO STRONGLY?

NO. I DON'T WANT TO DO THAT!

I SEE... IN THAT CASE, YOU COULD CHANGE YOUR PEN NAME AS WELL TO GET A FRESH START.

IT'S NOTHING WORTH BRAGGING ABOUT. AND I WANTED TO START AS A ROOKIE IN JUMP, SO...

I HAD A HUNCH THAT YOU WEREN'T AN AMATEUR WHEN I FIRST SAW YOUR WORK, BUT YOU SHOULD HAVE TOLD ME THAT YOU'VE HAD EXPERIENCE WITH A SERIES BEFORE.

NO, I'M SURE HE ISN'T THINKING THAT FAR AHEAD. IT MUST JUST BE HIS PRIDE FROM BEING A MANGA ARTIST FOR SUCH A LONG TIME...

MAYBE HE'S THINKING THAT IT WILL CREATE A LOT MORE BUZZ IF PEOPLE FIND OUT SOMEONE HIS AGE IS BEING PLACED IN JUMP FOR THE FIRST TIME?

DO YOU SERIOUSLY BELIEVE THAT A MAN MY AGE CAN HAVE A SERIES IN JUMP?

NEXT, SOME OF THE LINES SOUND A LITTLE OLD-FASHIONED TO ME. LET'S TWEAK THOSE A BIT.

I'D LIKE TO REVISE SOME LINES IN THE ONE-SHOT BEFORE WE DISCUSS A FUTURE SERIES.

OF COURSE I DO.

PLUS YOU'RE NOT SOME ROOKIE, YOU HAVE THE EXPERIENCE.

Pretty Soldier No.3
Mamako Magician
Age 16
Look 60cm
TD Htchi, Shishi, Shishi

FIRST, YOU PROBABLY WANT TO CHANGE THIS PRETTY SOLDIER TERM. THIS IS A RELATIVELY IMPORTANT TERM IN THE STORY, SO WE DON'T WANT TO USE STUFF THAT'S ALREADY BEEN USED IN OTHER WORKS.

OKAY.

OKAY.

SHFF

SURE...

HE SAID THAT WE'D TRY TO SUBMIT FOR THE SERIALIZATION MEETING IN MID-OCTOBER, SOON AFTER THE ONE-SHOT COMES OUT... THAT EDITOR IS A VERY PASSIONATE AND HARD-WORKING MAN.

I NEVER THOUGHT THE MEETING WOULD TAKE SO LONG...

SIX HOURS LATER

ARAI!

AZUMA SENSEI...

STAGGER...

THEY JUST DROPPED THE HAMMER ON ME. I'M NOT INCLUDED IN THEIR FUTURE PLANS.

NOT AT ALL. ALL OF MY SERIES HAVE BEEN DROPPED...

YOU'VE HAD MANY SERIES IN *JUMP* NOW, SO THE TABLES HAVE TURNED FOR BOTH OF US.

THE LAST TIME I SAW YOU WAS WHEN I WAS WORKING AS AN ASSISTANT FOR YOU... SO IT'S BEEN AT LEAST TEN YEARS, HASN'T IT...?

LONG TIME NO SEE.

AND STARTING FROM TODAY, I'M JOBLESS.

WHAT?

...

IT'S A CULT MANGA SETTING BUT DONE AS A MAINSTREAM BATTLE MANGA...

IT'S GOOD NO MATTER HOW MANY TIMES I READ IT... IT'S JUST LIKE HOW I FELT WHEN I READ *CLASSROOM OF TRUTH.* THEY BEAT ME TO IT!

TUESDAY, SEPTEMBER 27. WE WERE GIVEN A SAMPLE COPY OF ISSUE 44 WITH PANTY FLASH FIGHT IN IT.

I DON'T CARE IF YOU THINK IT'S PERVERTED. WE WANT TO SEE THOSE PANTIES! ESPECIALLY IF IT'S A CUTE GIRL OR A GIRL WE HAVE A CRUSH ON! ISN'T THAT RIGHT, SAIKO?!

I DON'T GET THE AUDIENCE'S REACTION. THEY'RE SUCH PERVERTS...

FINE, BUT JUST BECAUSE THEY'RE THE PANTIES OF SOME CUTE GIRL, WHY WOULD ANYONE GET SO EXCITED OVER THEM?

IT'S GOOD BECAUSE IT'S ABLE TO PRESENT SOMETHING SO STUPID IN SUCH A SERIOUS AND COMPELLING WAY! YOU DON'T WANT YOUR PANTIES BROADCASTED ALL OVER THE COUNTRY, DO YOU?! AND TO TOP IT OFF YOU HAVE TO TAKE YOUR PANTIES OFF WHEN YOU LOSE!!

BUT FIGHTING WHILE AVOIDING SHOWING YOUR PANTIES? TALK ABOUT LAME.

HEY... STOP IT! MASHIRO'S NOT GOING TO BE ABLE TO FALL ASLEEP TONIGHT IF HE HEARS ABOUT THAT!

THEN, I'LL TELL YOU! WHEN I STAYED OVER AT MIHO'S PLACE, MIHO'S PANTIES WERE...

HE'S IN A SITUATION WHERE HE CAN'T SEE THEM NO MATTER HOW MUCH HE WANTS TO.

OF COURSE HE DOES. BUT DON'T USE THEM AS AN EXAMPLE!

WHAT? MASHIRO TOO? THEN MASHIRO WANTS TO SEE MIHO'S PANTIES AS WELL?

BOOSH

174

OF COURSE I'M FIRED-UP. THE TV DRAMA STARTS NEXT WEEKEND.

BUT I STILL HAVEN'T GOTTEN FIRST PLACE.

SKRT SKRT

THE STORY'S BEEN AMAZING THESE DAYS TOO.

SKRT SKRT SKRT

YOU SEEM REALLY FIRED-UP, SENSEI.

高浜
TAKAHAMA

MUMBLE MUMBLE MUMBLE

MUMBLE MUMBLE...

IT'S NOT LIKE I'M GOING TO BE CALLED KAZUTAN EVEN IF I MOVE UP NOW.

AND IT'S JUST FOURTH PLACE TOO...

IN THIS WEEK'S EARLY RESULTS, YOU'VE FINALLY MOVED ABOVE PCP TO FOURTH PLACE.

PWOO——

IT'S ALL THANKS TO NAKAI.

——OF

UHH... HE GETS THE CREDIT...?

MNCH MNCH MNCH

Heh heh

VSH

IMPOSSIBLE.

HOW COULD I EVER BE POPULAR WITH THE GIRLS...!

I'D NEVER BE POPULAR EVEN IF I'M WEARING GLASSES

AND EVEN IF I WAS A WARLORD DURING THE WARRING STATES PERIOD IN MY PREVIOUS LIFE!

YOU'VE STARTED TO WIN MORE VOTES FROM FEMALE FANS EVER SINCE YOUR ARTWORK'S IMPROVED.

NO. THINGS ARE GOING EXACTLY AS I PLANNED.

WHAT DO YOU MEAN? YOU SOUND SO STUCK UP.

WHY YOU...!

IF YOU'RE TALKING ABOUT MAKING *CAN'T FOOL ME* INTO AN ANIME, I DON'T WANT TO HELP HIM ON THAT.

THIS IS YOUR CHANCE TO STUDY HOW TO MAKE A CHARACTER THAT WOULD LOOK GOOD EVEN IN AN ANIME AND IMPROVE YOUR OWN SKILLS AS WELL AS TEACH HIRAMARU THOSE SKILLS.

LOOK, NAKAI. YOU'RE A SKILLED ARTIST, BUT YOU'RE NO GOOD AT CREATING CHARACTERS.

GAH!

MNCH!

MNCH!

...

AS A MATTER OF FACT, MISS ERIKO IS SAID TO BE SLIGHTLY PRETTIER THAN AOKI SENSEI!

SHE'S AOKI SENSEI'S ELDER SISTER BY ONE YEAR. AND THEY'RE THE SPITTING IMAGE OF EACH OTHER TOO.

WHO'S THAT?

ERIKO?

NAKAI, HAVEN'T YOU HEARD OF MISS ERIKO?

...

WHAT?! I'VE HEARD SHE HAS A SISTER, BUT...

WHAT?!

PROPOSE!

DO WHAT?

HIRAMARU, I THINK YOU SHOULD DO IT ONCE *CAN'T FOOL ME* HAS BEEN ANIMATED.

THAT'S RIGHT. SHE'S HAS NOTHING TO DO WITH HIM...

B-BUT WHAT DOES MISS ERIKO HAVE TO DO WITH ME...?

I'VE BEEN TOLD THAT PEOPLE WHO DON'T KNOW THEM THAT WELL CAN ONLY DISTINGUISH THEM BY THE MOLE UNDER THEIR RIGHT OR LEFT EYE.

HEY... I AIN'T HELPING HIRAMARU GET MARRIED TO MISS AOKI!!

WHY YOU...!

AND THAT'S WHERE ERITAN COMES IN!!

THAT'S RIGHT! IF YOU WERE TO PROPOSE ON YOUR OWN, SHE'D REJECT YOU...

...BUT AS LONG AS YOU HAVE ME AS YOUR LOVE ADVISOR, SHE WILL ONLY ANSWER "YES"!

P-PRO-POSE TO YURI-TAN?!

BIN BOO—NG BII

NO... MR. YOSHIDA! PLEASE CONSIDER THINGS FROM THE POINT OF VIEW OF THE WOMAN BEING INTRODUCED TO NAKAI...

WHAT... ERITAN?!

I SHALL INTRO-DUCE YOU TO ERITAN!

AND BEHIND THAT MARRIAGE IS THE SUPER ASSISTANT AND FUTURE ELITE MANGA ARTIST, TAKURO NAKAI!

HER YOUNGER SISTER'S HAPPY MARRI-AGE!

BUT FOR THAT, YOU NEED TO GO ON A DIET FIRST!!

VSH

WOW, GREAT IDEAS ARE FLOW-ING!

I CAN'T STAND THAT!!

MR. NAKAI WOULD BE MY BROTHER-IN-LAW...!

WAIT... IF MR. NAKAI AND ERITAN ENDED UP GETTING MARRIED...

I-I'LL DO IT, MR. YOSHI-DA!

YOU HAVE A BRIGHT FUTURE IF YOU LET MR. YOSHIDA MANIPULATE YOU. I CAN VOUCH FOR THAT.

B-BUT IS IT REALLY GOING TO WORK...? I FEEL LIKE I'M BEING MANIPULATED.

WELL SAID, HIRA-MARU!

SMIRK

SHF SHF

NOOO OO!!

AARGH!!

OLDER MANGA ARTISTS? WHAT ARE YOU TALKING ABOUT?

THERE SEEMS TO BE A TREND WITH OLDER MANGA ARTISTS MAKING A COMEBACK RIGHT NOW.

...BY A LAND-SLIDE ?!

PANTY FLASH FIGHT GOT FIRST PLACE...

HUH ?!

DAMMIT, I MISSED OUT ON FIRST AGAIN!

WHAT ?! GIRI GOT THIRD PLACE ?!

WELL, IT WAS PRETTY GOOD.

PANTY SHOT IS AMAZING!!

SPLUB——

I DON'T EVEN REMEMBER WHO THAT IS!

AND YANAGI SENSEI?

WASN'T HE CANNED FROM HUSTLE BECAUSE HE KEPT TRYING TO MAKE MORE BASEBALL SERIES BUT THEY ALL FLOPPED?

NANGOKU SENSEI... THE ONE-HIT WONDER WITH THAT BASEBALL MANGA TWENTY YEARS AGO?

IT'S NOT JUST AZUMA SENSEI. NANGOKU SENSEI WHO WAS WORKING WITH MONTHLY HUSTLE AND YANAGI SENSEI WHO HAD A SERIES IN SHONEN KICK HAVE BROUGHT THEIR WORKS IN AS WELL.

HE'S BEEN A MANGA ARTIST FOR EIGHTEEN YEARS NOW... BUT HE'S NEVER HAD A HIT... OH, AND ARAI SENSEI, WHO WE CUT LOOSE LAST MONTH, CAME IN WITH A NEW PIECE OF WORK TOO...

KOFF

AND APPARENTLY, ALL OF THEIR WORKS WERE GOOD.

WHAT ?! DON'T TELL ME YOU'RE GOING TO PLACE THAT IN THE MAGAZINE! IT'S NOT GONNA BE SHONEN JUMP ANYMORE IF YOU START USING WORKS BY OLD MEN LIKE THAT!

UH...

...

AFTER ALL, WE'VE HAD TOO MANY PEOPLE SEE A LITTLE SUCCESS BUT THEN HAVE THEIR SERIES DROPPED SOON AFTER.

BUT IF THEIR WORKS GET PLACED IN THE MAGAZINE, IT ONLY MEANS THAT THE YOUNG CREATORS THESE DAYS AREN'T PULLING THEIR WEIGHT.

THAT'S UP TO THE PEOPLE ABOVE ME TO DECIDE. I CAN'T SAY ANYTHING ABOUT IT.

THE NEXT TUES-DAY

?

IT'S FUKUDA.

CHIK

♪

NOW WE'VE GOT VETERANS FROM ALL FOUR MAJOR SHONEN MAGAZINES! WHAT THE HECK IS THE EDITORIAL DEPARTMENT THINKING?!

ARAI SENSEI, NANGOKU SENSEI WHO WORKED IN *HUSTLE*, YANAGI SENSEI WHO WORKED IN *KICK*, AND AZUMA SENSEI AGAIN, WHO USED TO WORK IN *THREE*.

NOT AT ALL...

NO...

DID YOU HEAR ABOUT THE THREE ONE-SHOTS IN THE NOVEMBER ISSUES?!

WHAT GOOD IS IT TO GIVE THEM A CHANCE?!

MAYBE THEY DECIDED TO GIVE VETERAN MANGA ARTISTS A CHANCE FOR A CHANGE...?

THAT'S A GOOD POINT, BUT THERE'S NOTHING I CAN DO ABOUT IT...

IT WON'T BE *SHONEN JUMP* ANYMORE IF THEY THROW IN SO MANY WORKS BY OLD MEN! WHAT IS THIS, *GEEZER JUMP*?!

THESE AIN'T LONG-RUNNING CREATORS WHO'VE PRODUCED GREAT RESULTS FOR *JUMP*, YOU KNOW!

MR. HATTORI...

MAYBE THEY'RE TRYING TO SHAKE UP THE YOUNG CREATORS ...?

LIKE FUKUDA SAID, YOUNG PEOPLE LIKE US HAVE TO WORK HARDER...

HMM... IT'S LIKE A MANGA ARTISTS OF THE PAST REVIVAL... MAYBE THE EDITORIAL DEPARTMENT WANTS THIS TO GET PUBLICITY?

OH, IT'S A PHONE CALL TO ME THIS TIME...

!

STARTING WITH THE NOVEMBER 21 ISSUE?!

WHAT?! *PANTY FLASH FIGHT* ☞ IS GOING TO GET A SHORT-TERM SERIALIZA-TION?!

THREE ONE-SHOTS BY VETERAN MANGA ARTISTS AND A SHORT-TERM SERIES BY AZUMA SENSEI... WHAT'S GOING ON...?

OH, YES. I UNDER-STAND...

MY WORK SCHEDULE IS GOING TO BE RATHER TIGHT, SO PLEASE KEEP UP YOUR CURRENT WORK PACE.

THIS WILL ONLY BE TEMPORARY BUT I'M GOING TO BE IN CHARGE OF THREE WORKS.

...

YEAH. THE RESULT OF THE ONE-SHOT WAS OUTSTANDING, AND HE HAD ALREADY CREATED THE SERIES STORYBOARDS, SO WE CAME TO A QUICK DECISION ON IT.

16 Rookie and Veteran (The End)

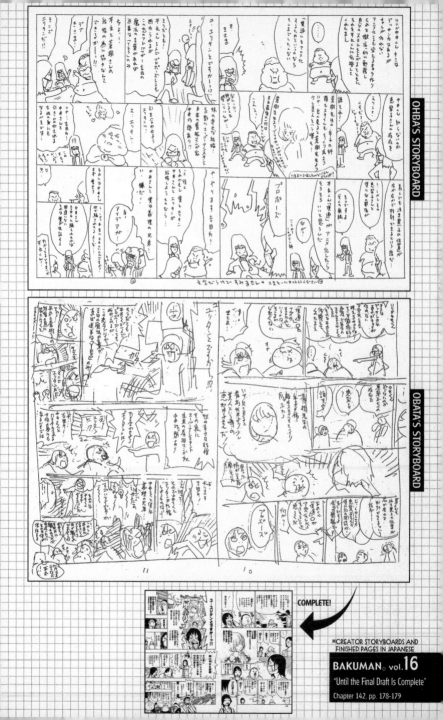

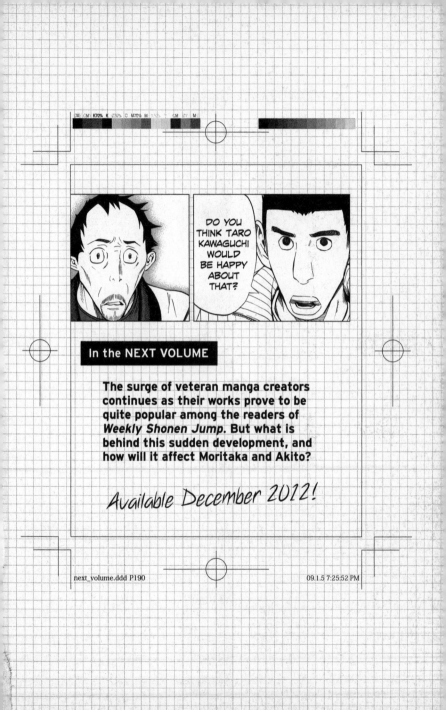

DO YOU THINK TARO KAWAGUCHI WOULD BE HAPPY ABOUT THAT?

In the NEXT VOLUME

The surge of veteran manga creators continues as their works prove to be quite popular among the readers of *Weekly Shonen Jump*. But what is behind this sudden development, and how will it affect Moritaka and Akito?

Available December 2012!

This is the LAST PAGE

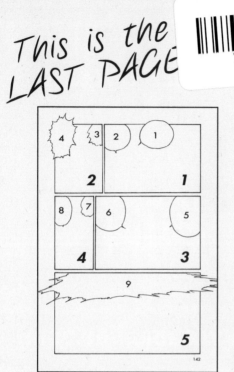

← Follow the action this way.

BAKUMAN。 has been printed in the original Japanese format in order to preserve the orientation of the original artwork.

Please turn it around and begin reading from right to left. Unlike English, Japanese is read right to left, so Japanese comics are read in reverse order from the way English comics are typically read. Have fun with it!